By 1794, the balloon had become a weapon of war when the French used a tethered one to direct tactics at the Battle of Fleurus. However, it was during the American Civil War that the balloon came into its own. Balloons were used by both sides to observe the enemy and many of the balloonists took the risk of untethered flight over the enemy lines to cover as much ground as possible.

HOTSPUR

BOOK FOR BOYS 1989

CONTENTS

Printed and Published in Great Britain by D. C. THOMSON & CO., LTD.,
185 Fleet Street, London EC4A 2HS.

ISBN 0-85116-420-X.

John One

SCOURGE OF THE TECHNOLORDS

The Catastrophe . . . laid waste to Earth in the 21st Century and life has returned to medieval ways.

The People . . . eke a living from the scorched earth around the far-flung settlements, ruled over by ruthless **Technolords** who control the remnants of 21st Century technology.

Teachers . . . survivors of the 'intelligentsia' who were blamed for The Catastrophe and slaughtered in its wake. Only *they* fully understand the technology.

And then there are . . . **The Ones,** the only free men; skilled survivors who need the protection of no settlement wall, who bow the knee to no master.

John One is such a man . . .

CHAPTER ONE
Quest
Dawn . . . in a Settlement in the North West Sector—
BRING HIM OUT! HAND OVER YOUR TEACHER!
DAYBREAKERS— TECHNOLORD BORK'S TROOPS. RUN! SAVE YOURSELVES—
WELL, ELDER— WHERE IS HE?
SIR—WE ARE POOR AND HUNGRY. YOU CAN SURELY SEE WE HAVE NO TEACHER TO HELP US—!
DON'T LIE TO ME, PIG—I HAVE EYES IN MY HEAD . . .
AAARRGH!
. . . THAT IS A WIND POWER-GENERATOR. ONLY A TEACHER COULD HAVE TAUGHT YOU HOW TO BUILD SUCH A THING!
NO, NO—THAT IS NOT SO, SIR. IT—
Nearby . . . John One and his faithful companion, Kol—
IF THE SETTLERS DO HAVE A TEACHER, KOL . . . HE COULD BE THE ONE I SEEK.
MY LONG-BOW MUST SING, KOL . . .

John One's long-bow sang and his aim was true. Again and again his arrows sped to their targets.
NNN-UH!
AH-EE-EE!
HOLD FAST, MEN — THERE IS ONLY ONE MAN. GUN HIM DOWN — !
ROOAARR!
One man and . . . Kol! Fang and claw bared, the black panther leaped to his master's defence . . .
BY THE STARS — ! AAH — NO-O . . .
UNH!
Arrow, fang and claw did their work . . . till the last Daybreaker fell.
IT IS OVER, KOL. THIS SETTLEMENT IS SAFE . . .
NOW WHERE IS YOUR TEACHER? BRING HIM OUT —
IF WE WOULD NOT SURRENDER HIM TO THE DAYBREAKERS, WE WILL NOT SURRENDER HIM TO A BRIG-ONE —
A BRIG-ONE!? YOU TAKE ME FOR A BRIGAND, A THIEF! AFTER I HAVE SAVED YOUR LIVES —
I DON'T, STRANGER. I AM THE TEACHER. WHAT DO YOU WANT WITH ME?

YOU ARE THE — ? THEN I WANT NOTHING. YOU ARE NOT THE ONE I SEEK. YOU ARE NOT MY FATHER . . .
BUT HEAR THIS, TEACHER. TECHNOLORD BORK KNOWS YOU ARE HERE. HIS MEN WILL RETURN. LEAVE HERE — SOON — !
'STRANGER' THEY CALL ME, KOL. AND 'JOHN' IS JUST A NAME I GAVE MYSELF. BUT WHO AM I IN TRUTH — ?
I KNOW ONLY THAT MY FATHER WAS A SCIENTIST. I HAVE NOT SEEN HIM SINCE I WAS A TOT . . .
BUT HE SURVIVED THE SLAUGHTER. HE IS ALIVE — I FEEL IT IN MY BLOOD. I WILL NOT REST TILL I FIND HIM — !
Suddenly a warning light flashed on the power-trike—
THE POWER-CELL IS RUNNING LOW. I MUST REPLACE IT SOON.
AND OUT HERE IN THE BARREN-LANDS MY ONLY HOPE IS A DAYBREAKER RECCE-PATROL. THEIR VEHICLES USE THE SAME KIND OF POWER-CELL . . .
John One knew from experience the most likely places to find Daybreaker Recce-Patrols and soon—
THEY'RE SCANNING THE AREA FOR TELL-TALE SIGNS OF A TEACHER. IF THEY FIND ONE, THEY CALL UP A PUNIC-PATROL LIKE THE ONE WE HAVE JUST DEALT WITH.
At John One's signal, Kol moved off silently, then . . .

AA-AAAH — !
A BRIG-ONE ATTACK! DEFEND YOURSELVES —
THEY MUST BE UP THERE — ON THE RISE . . .
But *John One* was moving in all the time and so was *Kol* . . .
AAI-AI-EE!
DIE, LACKEYS OF THE TECHNOLORD!
IT IS DONE — OH, NO! THERE WAS A *FIFTH* DAYBREAKER . . . IN THE VEHICLE CONTROL CABIN — !
ROARRR!
HE MUST NOT ESCAPE. WITHOUT POWER-CELLS I AM STRANDED . . .
. . . HELPLESS ON FOOT IN THE DREAD BARREN-LANDS.
AAARGHNNNGH!
A DEAD HAND AT THE CONTROLS. NOW I HAVE TWENTY SECONDS TO GET THE POWER-CELL . . .
CRUNK!
SCREEEEECHHH!

Twenty seconds . . . fifteen . . . John One ran like the wind . . .
ALL DAYBREAKER VEHICLES ARE PROGRAMMED TO SELF-DESTRUCT WHEN ATTACKED, TO PREVENT THEM FALLING INTO BRIG-ONES' HANDS —
Ten seconds . . . five . . . his fingers worked nimbly on the power-cell connections . . .
BACK, KOL! BACK — ! ANY SECOND NOW —
BROUM!
GOT IT — AA-AAH! — AND JUST IN TIME TOO . . .
The blast blew John One over a sheer drop!
BY THE STARS! MORE TROUBLE —
Clutching the precious power-cell to him, John One hauled himself up one-handed. And when he had regained his breath—
A SETTLEMENT HIDDEN IN THE TREES. SO THAT'S WHAT THE RECCE-PATROL WAS INTERESTED IN . . . THAT AND THE STRANGE PIPELINE THERE! I KNOW WHAT THAT IS . . .
It took John One only a few minutes to replace his dying power-cell. Then he collected Kol, issued a command which sent the intelligent beast loping ahead through cover, and sped towards the Settlement—
HOLD IT, STRANGER. YOU'RE NOT WELCOME HERE.
NO — BACK OFF, BRIG-ONE, WHILE YOU STILL BREATHE!
I'M NO BRIG. I BRING A WARNING FOR YOUR TEACHER.

TEACHER? WHO SAYS WE HAVE A TEACHER — ?
METHINKS WE'D BETTER SILENCE THIS SCUM — NOW — !
NOT SO FAST, FRIENDS . . .

GRRRRR!
ALLOW ME TO INTRODUCE MY HUNGRY COMPANION, KOL!
NOW . . . TAKE ME TO THE SETTLEMENT ELDERS — OR YOU'LL BE KOL'S DINNER.

Reluctantly the guard took John One to the Elders—
OLD MEN, THE ILL-DISGUISED SYSTEM OF PIPES OUTSIDE YOUR WALLS IS OBVIOUSLY A CRUDE METHANE GAS PLANT. THAT MEANS YOU HAVE A TEACHER —
SO YOU COME TO BLACKMAIL US — ?
WE PAY — OR YOU WILL BETRAY OUR TEACHER TO THE TECHNOLORDS— !

FOOLS! I COULD DO THAT WITHOUT SETTING FOOT HERE? I WANT ONLY TO TALK TO THE TEACHER.

Just then . . . danger threatened! At the Daybreakers' H.Q. the control room officer had noticed that one of their Recce-Patrols was missing—
WHEN DID PATROL X.15 LAST REPORT IN — ?
LITTLE OVER A HALF-BREAK AGO — FROM HERE, ON THE SOUTHERN EDGE OF THE BARREN-LANDS —

COMMANDER — THERE IS A SETTLEMENT JUST TO THE NORTH . . .
SEND IN A PUNIC-PATROL!

Back at the Settlement—
WE HAVE DISCUSSED. IT IS DECIDED. WE WILL BRING THE TEACHER TO YOU . . .

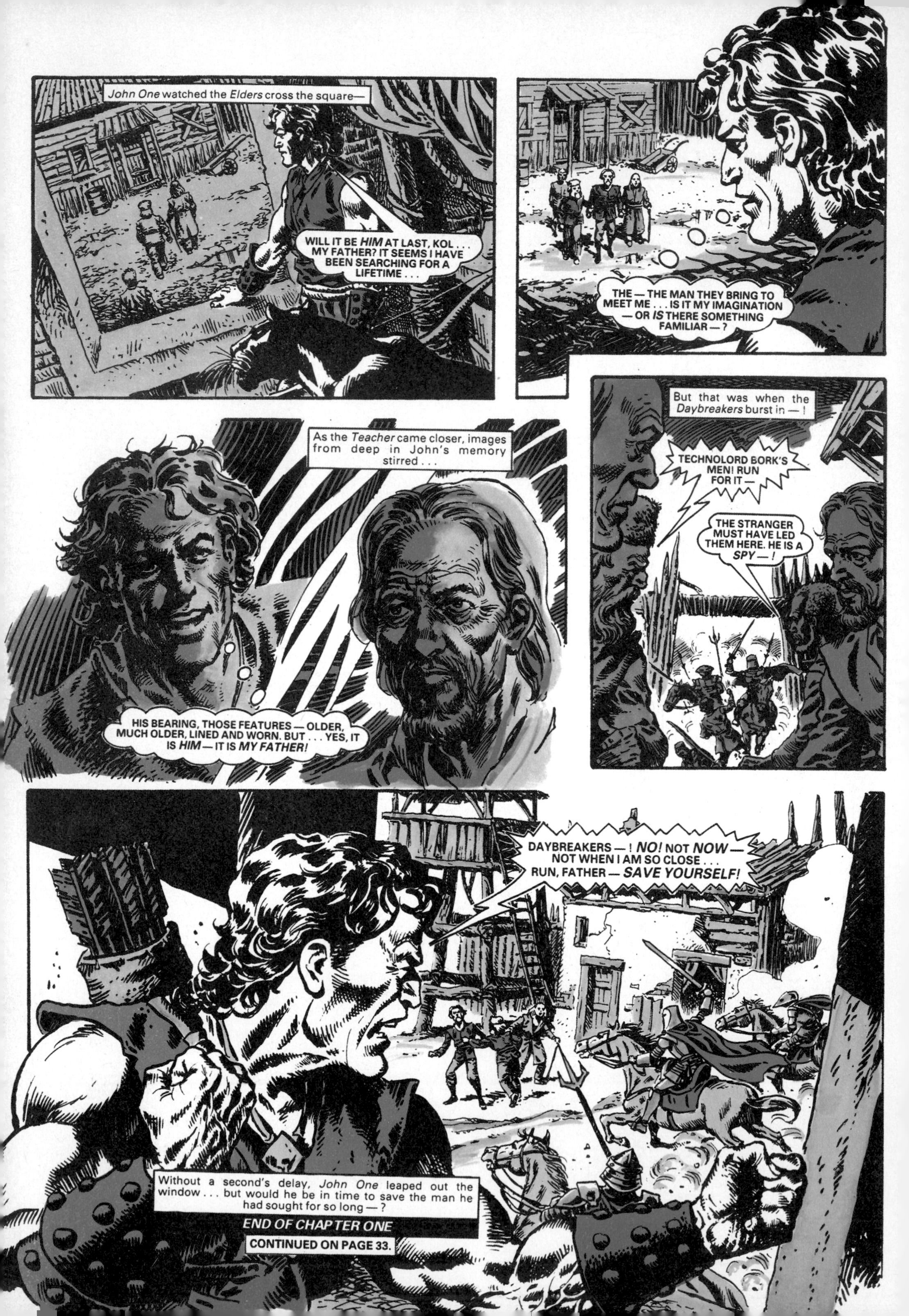

DAYBREAKERS — ! *NO!* NOT *NOW* — NOT WHEN I AM SO CLOSE . . . RUN, FATHER — *SAVE YOURSELF!*

Without a second's delay, *John One* leaped out the window . . . but would he be in time to save the man he had sought for so long — ?

END OF CHAPTER ONE

CONTINUED ON PAGE 33.

THE MEDAL
Reared in Denmark before the Second World War, Kurt Svensen was a big powerful youth but he lacked one thing — courage! He was shown up when he fell out with one of the young sons of a fellow fisherman . . .
NO, NO! DON'T HIT ME AGAIN!
LEAVE ME ALONE! JUST LEAVE ME ALONE!
GET UP, KURT! YOU'VE SHAMED YOUR FAMILY ENOUGH FOR ONE DAY!
A week later.
FISHING IS A HARD LIFE, KURT, AND TO FACE THE SEA IN ALL ITS MOODS NEEDS COURAGE! YOU DON'T HAVE IT! I FEEL IT WOULD BE BEST IF YOU LEFT HERE!
ANYTHING YOU SAY, FATHER!
A LITTLE MONEY FOR YOUR JOURNEY, MY SON! I DO NOT CARE WHERE YOU GO, BUT DO NOT COME BACK TILL YOU HAVE FOUND SOME COURAGE!
RØY

Kurt wandered about Europe till he grew to manhood but found no courage. Eventually he found himself outside the French Foreign Legion fort in Marseilles . . .
THE FOREIGN LEGION, EH? PERHAPS I'LL FIND SOME COURAGE IN THE ARMY!
Kurt did not find life easy in the Legion — nor did he find his courage!
FIGHT BACK, COWARD! WILL NOTHING MAKE YOU FIGHT?
When the Second World War came, the Legion found itself fighting for both sides. Some legionnaires fought with the Free French on the Allied side, others with the Vichy French on the side of the Germans. In Syria, legionnaire fought legionnaire!
COME, COWARD, WE HAVE TO WITHDRAW. OUR COMRADES ON THE OTHER SIDE ARE TOO STRONG FOR US!
NOW'S MY CHANCE! I'LL HIDE IN THE CELLAR UNTIL THE OTHERS COME — THEN I'LL SURRENDER! I'VE HAD ENOUGH OF THIS WAR.
I'LL BE SAFE HERE!
I SURRENDER! DON'T KILL ME, I BEG YOU! DON'T SHOOT!
WE WON'T KILL YOU, MY LITTLE COWARD! YOU ARE JUST WHAT WE'VE BEEN LOOKING FOR.
LEGIONNAIRE, WE DO NOT INTEND TO HARM YOU. WE WISH TO COME OVER TO THE FREE FRENCH — BE SO GOOD AS TO ACCEPT OUR SURRENDER!
BUT . . . BUT . . . YOU DO NOT UNDERSTAND . . .
THIS IS NOT WHAT I MEANT TO HAPPEN! I WANT OUT OF THIS WAR!

But Kurt did not get out of the war. With a lot of legionnaires he ended up in Bir Hacheim where the Free French garrison was surrounded by the German Afrika Korps.

Svensen had grabbed a haversack of grenades!

ACHTUNG! KILL THAT MANIAC.
YOU CRAZY FELLOW!
URGH!
I AM HURT — URGH! WHY DO I DO THIS MAD THING?
IS IT POSSIBLE I HAVE FOUND COURAGE?
CORPORAL, WHY DID THAT IDIOT DANE DO IT?
TO EARN HIS MEDAL. HE WAS AN HONEST AND HONOURABLE MAN WHO FOUND HIS COURAGE WHEN IT MATTERED MOST!
The End

X-BOW
X-Bow, the world's most amazing crime fighter, had urgent business on Shark Island, Floriday . . .
SHARK ISLAND
CAUSWAY CLOSED
GO VIA FERRY
HEY, IT'S X-BOW! WE GOTTA STOP HIM!
YEH, HE HASN'T SEEN THE WARNING!
SORRY, FELLAS, I'VE GOT MY JUMP JETS ON! I'VE GOT URGENT BUSINESS WITH YOUR BOSS!
G . . .GEE, LOOK AT THAT!
THE RIPPER SURE MADE A MESS OF THAT CAUSEWAY!
X-Bow made his way to the beach of the holiday town of Punta Sarbi . . .
SHARK! SHARK!
IT LOOKS LIKE I'M JUST IN TIME TO STOP THE RIPPER DOING A LOT WORSE!

B

GOOD JOB I BROUGHT A SHARK REPELLANT BOLT IN MY BOW!
RIGHT ON HIS SNOUT! THAT'LL DISCOURAGE HIM!
DRAT! TOO LATE! DRURY'S ALREADY SENT FOR X-BOW. COME, RIPPER, MY PRECIOUS ONE, THERE IS NO TIME TO WASTE!
WE MUST BRING OUR MAIN OPERATION FORWARD — TO TODAY!
PHEW, X-BOW — THANK GOODNESS I SENT FOR YOU! NO ONE EXPECTED THE RIPPER WOULD BURST THROUGH THE STEEL MESH!
AH, YOU MUST BE POLICE CHIEF DRURY!
THAT'S RIGHT. OUR LOCAL COUNCIL VOTED AGAINST SEEKING YOUR HELP BUT I WENT AHEAD AND SENT FOR YOU!
AND THAT'S WHY RIPPER SINGLED YOU OUT.
BECAUSE OF YOUR WATERPROOF WATCH!
THAT'S CRAZY! HOW COULD A SHARK . . . ?

IT'S BUGGED!
WHAT?
BLEEP BLEEP
X-Bow quickly took the watch apart . . .
SOMEBODY SLIPPED THIS DEVICE INSIDE WHILE YOU HAD YOUR WATCH OFF SOMETIME! THE RIPPER WAS PROGRAMMED TO HOME IN ON IT. SOMEBODY WANTED TO STOP YOU SENDING FOR ME — BUT THEY WERE TOO LATE. NOW I MUST DASH!
THAT HELICOPTER'S BEEN CIRCLING! THE RIPPER'S MASTER MUST BE ABOARD!
THEY'RE HEADING INTO THE MANGROVES. I'LL HAVE TO FOLLOW THEM!
THIS STRIP OF LAND LEADS INTO THE SWAMP.
DRAT! X-BOW'S FOLLOWING US! I'LL HAVE TO DEAL WITH HIM!

KILL THE INTRUDER, SWIFT-AXE!

HOWLING BOBCATS! WHAT WAS THAT?

WAAAH . . . OH! I'VE LOST CONTROL!

YAAAAANGH!
HOTDOG! A MAD SEMINOLE!

WAAAAAH!

The Indian quickly recovered . . .
I KILL!
WHAT'S THAT METAL PIECE ON HIS HEADBAND?
LET'S SEE WHAT HAPPENS WHEN IT COMES OFF!
WHO ARE YOU? WHAT DO I DO? WHAT IS THIS KNIFE?
YOU WERE TRYING TO KILL ME, THAT'S ALL!
RADIO SIGNALS THROUGH THE PRONGS ON THIS MINI-RECEIVER TURNED YOU INTO A ZOMBIE! YOU HAD TO OBEY YOUR MASTER'S EVERY COMMAND!
THEN BEWARE. OTHERS HAVE THESE MAGIC BANDS! SOME OF MY OWN PEOPLE!
X-Bow sent the Seminole for help and carried on to the middle of the swamp . . .
A RADIO-CONTROLLED SHARK, THEN AN INDIAN AND NOW A SNAKE! WHAT WILL COME UP NEXT?
TRY THAT! IT'S AN INSTANT TRANQUILISER GAS!

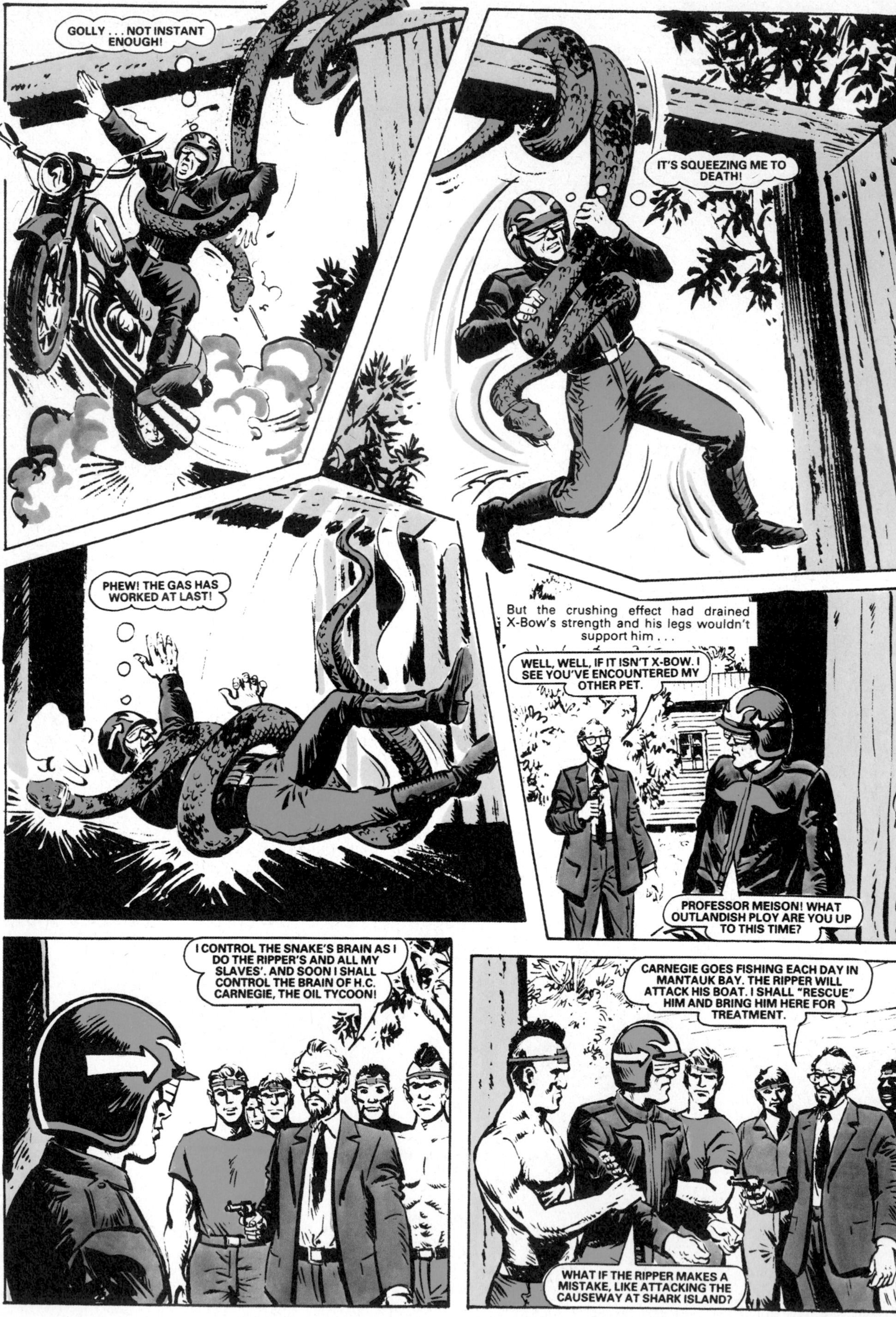

GOLLY . . . NOT INSTANT ENOUGH!

IT'S SQUEEZING ME TO DEATH!

PHEW! THE GAS HAS WORKED AT LAST!

But the crushing effect had drained X-Bow's strength and his legs wouldn't support him . . .

WELL, WELL, IF IT ISN'T X-BOW. I SEE YOU'VE ENCOUNTERED MY OTHER PET.

PROFESSOR MEISON! WHAT OUTLANDISH PLOY ARE YOU UP TO THIS TIME?

AH, YES! AT THE VERY BEGINNING HE RAN AMOK, BUT NO MORE! SOON I SHALL HAVE ALL THE MONEY IN THE WORLD TO FINANCE MY EXPERIMENTS!

I MUST GO NOW. LATER, I SHALL FEED YOU TO THE RIPPER!

X-Bow heard Meison's helicopter taking off as he struggled with his bonds . . .
MEISON'S GONE BUT I'M FREE NOW! AND JUST IN TIME. SOMEBODY'S COMING.

SORRY, PAL! I'VE NO TIME TO LOSE!

He found his bike and bow outside and set out after Meison . . .
GATE'S CLOSED! HAVE TO GO OVER!
IT'S CHIEF DRURY IN A POLICE CHOPPER! THAT ROPE WILL GIVE ME A LIFT!

THE SEMINOLE RELAYED YOUR MESSAGE, X-BOW! WHERE DO WE GO?
HEAD FOR MANTAUK BAY!
Meantime . . .
MAYDAY! MAYDAY! WE'RE BEING ATTACKED BY A MAD SHARK!
THE FAIR HORIZON
A RIFLE'S NO USE!
WE'RE SAVED, MISTER CARNEGIE! LOOK!
NOW TO PLAY THE GOOD SAMARITAN! BUT I SHALL ONLY RESCUE CARNEGIE! THE RIPPER MAY HAVE THE OTHERS!
JUMP JETS ON! CUTTING LOOSE, CHIEF!
X-BOW! THE RIPPER SHALL HAVE HIM SOONER THAN I INTENDED!
A TOUCH OF TRANQULISERS FOR YOU, RIPPER!

THAT'S DONE IT! THE BOLT WILL FALL OUT LATER.

I'LL KILL HIM!
GET DOWN!

THE X-BOW SURFACE-TO-AIR MISSILE SHOULD PUT PAID TO HIM FOR GOOD!

WELL, THAT'S SAVED YOU AND YOUR FORTUNE, MISTER CARNEGIE.

X-Bow and Carnegie were taken off by the police helicopter as a coastguard vessel arrived to pick up the others . . .
MEISON WOULD HAVE DRUGGED YOU AND INSERTED A TINY RECEIVER IN YOUR BRAIN. YOU'D HAVE RETURNED TO BUSINESS NONE THE WISER! WHENEVER HE NEEDED A CHEQUE A RADIO SIGNAL WOULD HAVE MADE YOU SIGN. EVERYONE WOULD HAVE THOUGHT YOU WERE DOING IT FROM GRATITUDE.

The Ripper disappeared into the vastness of the ocean and, Meison's slaves were released then . . .
THIS CHEQUE IS FOR YOU, X-BOW. WHAT WILL YOU DO WITH IT?
SOME OF IT WILL GO TO FIGHTING CRIME! THE REST, I THINK, IN PREVENTING CRUELTY TO THE GIANTS OF THE DEEP.
The End

The COONSKIN GRENADIER

After inheriting a Royal Warrant that made him an Honorary Colonel in the British Royal Grenadiers, hill-billy Zebadiah Flood was eager to do his duty during the Second World War. However, Colonel Sir John Grogan kept finding him lots of jobs in far away places — which is how Zeb, Alexander the ape, Lightning the hound, and Sergeant Major Minchin happened to be aboard a Royal Navy supply ship when it was torpedoed off the Bahamas.

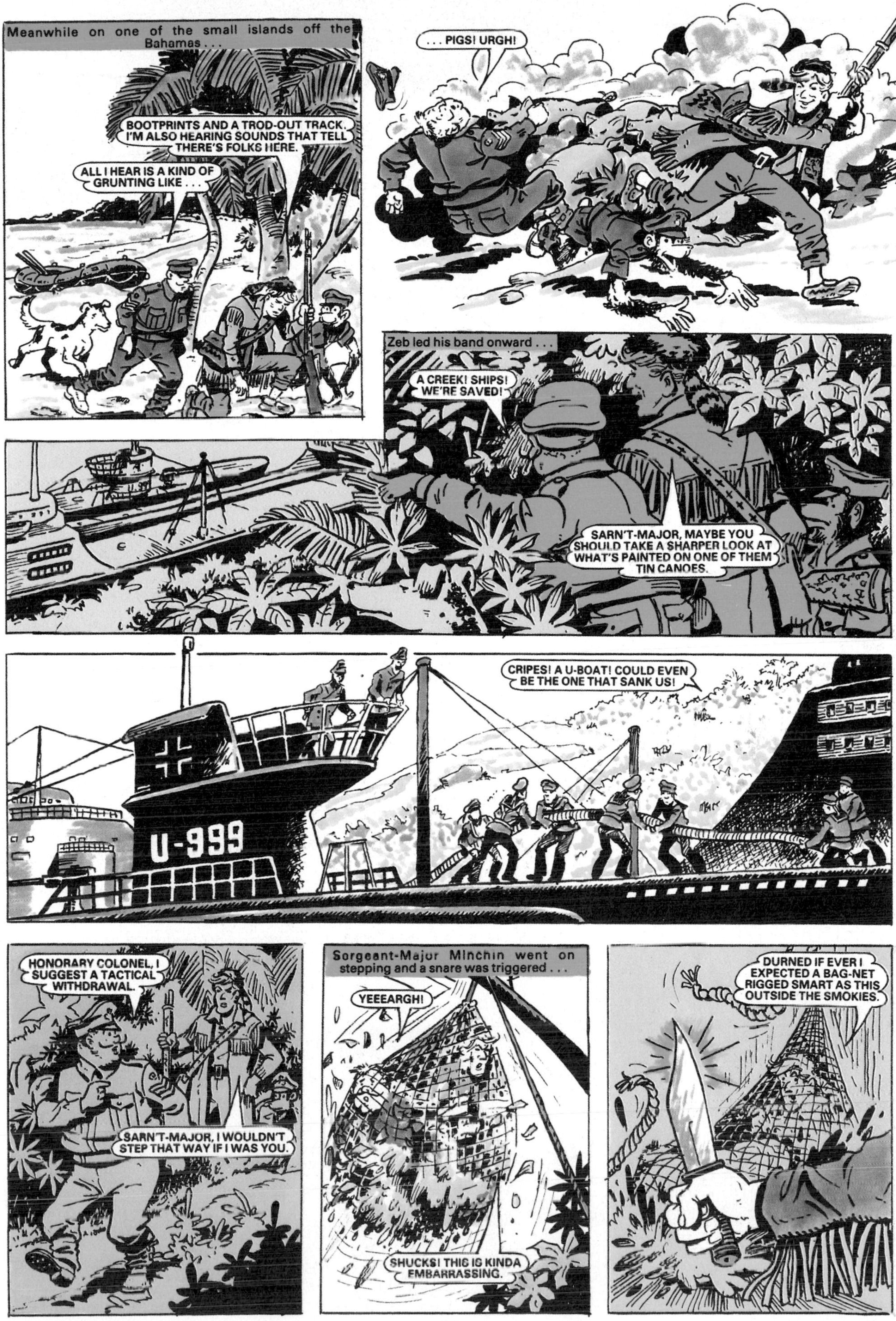

Meanwhile on one of the small islands off the Bahamas . . .

BOOTPRINTS AND A TROD-OUT TRACK. I'M ALSO HEARING SOUNDS THAT TELL THERE'S FOLKS HERE.

ALL I HEAR IS A KIND OF GRUNTING LIKE . . .

. . . PIGS! URGH!

Zeb led his band onward . . .

A CREEK! SHIPS! WE'RE SAVED!

SARN'T-MAJOR, MAYBE YOU SHOULD TAKE A SHARPER LOOK AT WHAT'S PAINTED ON ONE OF THEM TIN CANOES.

U-999

CRIPES! A U-BOAT! COULD EVEN BE THE ONE THAT SANK US!

Zeb's band was marched off under escort.

Zeb was interrupted . . .

The shore party departed slightly battered and bruised.

YOU'VE DONE SALUTED LONG ENOUGH, ALEXANDER. NOW LOWER IT.

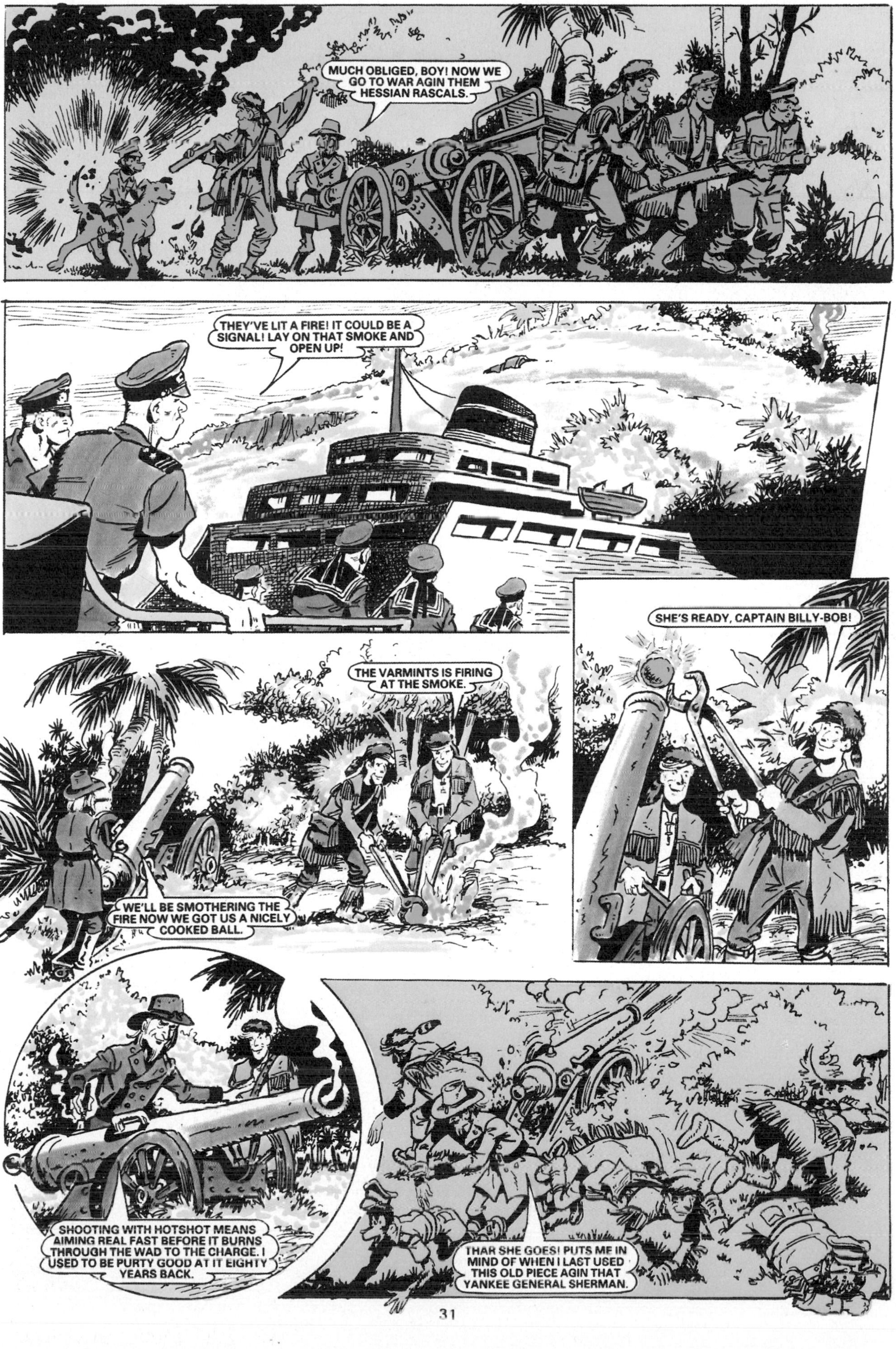

THEY'VE LIT A FIRE! IT COULD BE A SIGNAL! LAY ON THAT SMOKE AND OPEN UP!

THE VARMINTS IS FIRING AT THE SMOKE.

WE'LL BE SMOTHERING THE FIRE NOW WE GOT US A NICELY COOKED BALL.

SHE'S READY, CAPTAIN BILLY-BOB!

SHOOTING WITH HOTSHOT MEANS AIMING REAL FAST BEFORE IT BURNS THROUGH THE WAD TO THE CHARGE. I USED TO BE PURTY GOOD AT IT EIGHTY YEARS BACK.

THAR SHE GOES! PUTS ME IN MIND OF WHEN I LAST USED THIS OLD PIECE AGIN THAT YANKEE GENERAL SHERMAN.

Fuel ignited by the hotshot exploded and the tanker and U-boat were overwhelmed by a rush of flame . . .
U-999

Offshore an American destroyer was hunting for the U-boat.
GUNFIRE AND NOW ONE HECK OF A BLAZE! WE HAD BETTER GO CHECK ON IT.

A GOLDURN YANKEE FLAG! CHILD, ARE WE REALLY TIED UP WITH THEM VARMINTS?
WE SURE ARE, SUH!

Captain Billy-Bob Flood came to a big decision . . .
YANKEE, THE CAROLINE SCOUTS IS WILLING TO TALK TERMS TO END THIS HERE WAR BETWEEN THE NORTH AND THE SOUTH.
HUH — WHAT?

NOW WE CAN HITCH A RIDE BACK TO HELP SIR JOHN WITH THE WAR, SARN'T-MAJOR. I CAN IMAGINE THE PURE JOY ON HIS FACE WHEN HE GETS THE NEWS.
YESSIR . . . SO CAN I!
The End

CONTINUED FROM PAGE 12.

CHAPTER TWO Duel

John One smashed the window and leaped to the rescue —

THE DAYBREAKERS SHALL NOT HAVE HIM, KOL — NOT AFTER ALL WE'VE BEEN THROUGH — !

NN-UGH — !

COME ON, SETTLERS — *FIGHT!* WILL YOU FOREVER BOW TO THE TYRANTS?

THE STRANGER IS RIGHT! LET US FIGHT FOR OUR FREEDOM —

EE-AARGH!

THEY RESIST! CUT THEM DOWN BEFORE THEY ORGANISE — AND SOMEONE SETTLE THAT BIG CAT'S HASH — !

KOL — ! BE STILL, FRIEND — I WILL RELEASE YOU WHEN I CAN —
— AS SOON AS I AM RID OF THESE TORMENTORS!
NNNGH!
In spite of John One's heroic resistance, the Daybreakers were gaining the upper hand —
COWARDLY SWINE — YOU WOULD NOT DARE RAISE YOUR LANCE TO KOL IF HE WERE FREE . . .
GET THE TEACHER OUT OF HERE. I'LL DEAL WITH THAT REBEL FOOL — !
AARRGH!
John One fell to a crippling blast of energy from the Daybreaker officer's weapon . . .
LEARN FROM THIS DAY, SCUM — RESISTANCE TO THE TECHNOLORD IS FUTILE!
MY SON, MY SON — THEY HAVE SLAIN HIM!
MY WHOLE FAMILY . . . WIPED OUT — !

HIS FAULT! HE BROUGHT THIS DISASTER UPON US —

AYE! HE LED THE USELESS RESISTANCE! KILL HIM — !

LEAVE HIM TO ME . . .

COME ON, YOU STINKING BRIG. GET UP AND FIGHT — OR SHOULD I KILL YOU WHERE YOU LIE — ?

UH — ?

COME ON, PIG — MAKE A FIGHT OF IT — !

AA-UNH!

Gravely injured by the energy-blast, *John One* was in no condition to walk, far less FIGHT . . .

. . . and the *Settler-guard* had no intention of allowing him time to recover!

The sight of the cowardly and vicious treatment of his master lent *Kol* the strength to break free of the net —

GRRAA-AAR!

AIEE-EE — !

NO — NO MORE KILLING, KOL. WE GO. THEY ARE COWARDS, BUT PERHAPS THEY ARE RIGHT . . .

PERHAPS WE *DID* BRING DISASTER UPON THEM.

Crippled and ravaged by pain and sapping weakness, the journey over rough tracks was too much for *John One*. Finally his strength gave out —
AA-AAH . . .

Kol was powerless to prevent his master plunging down a rocky slope to a river.

But the intelligent beast was quick to act to save him from drowning by dragging him out of the water.

Kol could do no more than stand guard over his master as he hovered between life and death. An hour later . . . a band of *Brig-Ones* happened by. They were thieves and cut-throats who survived by preying on defenceless *Settlers*.
WHOEVER HE IS, HE'S NOT DEAD, VORN — I SAW HIM MOVE JUST NOW.
LOOKS LIKE A BRIG LIKE US, TERGOL. BUT I'M NOT INTERESTED IN HIM — IT'S THAT MACHINE OF HIS THAT I HAVE MY EYE ON . . .

Kol did not attack as the *Brigs* approached. It was as if he were 'sizing them up', realising they might be *John One's* only chance of survival . . .
THAT BEAST LOOKS VICIOUS, VORN!
EASY, BOY. WE MEAN YOU NO HARM . . .

ONE OF YOU GRAB THE TRIKE — LOOKS LIKE THE BEAST WILL LET US AWAY WITH IT AS LONG AS WE TAKE CARE OF ITS MASTER . . .

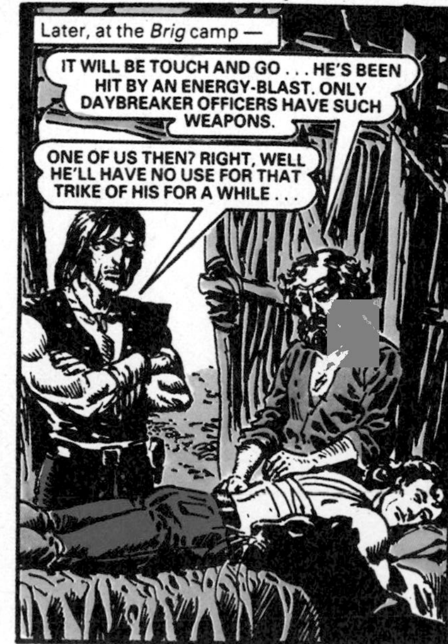
Later, at the *Brig* camp —
IT WILL BE TOUCH AND GO . . . HE'S BEEN HIT BY AN ENERGY-BLAST. ONLY DAYBREAKER OFFICERS HAVE SUCH WEAPONS.
ONE OF US THEN? RIGHT, WELL HE'LL HAVE NO USE FOR THAT TRIKE OF HIS FOR A WHILE . . .

HANDS OFF THAT TRIKE, TERGOL. IT BELONGS BY RIGHT TO *ME* AS LEADER — !
AA-AH! I WAS ONLY *LOOKING*, VORN . . .
IT'S MINE WHETHER THE GUY LIVES OR DIES — UNLESS HE FANCIES *FIGHTING* FOR IT, EH — ?
NO CHANCE OF *THAT*, VORN — HE'S A GONER FOR SURE.
THE SETTLEMENT'S WIDE OPEN — GRAB WHAT YOU CAN, MEN!
As the *Brig-Ones'* doctor fought to bring *John One* back from the edge of death, the days ran into weeks. And all the while, *Vorn* was making full use of the *power-trike*. Led by *Vorn* on his powerful new fighting-machine, the cut-throat band roamed far and wide, striking terror into defenceless *Settlers* and armed *Daybreakers* alike.
OUT OF MY WAY, FOOL! YOUR FASTEST HORSEMAN WON'T CATCH ME ON *THIS* MEAN MACHINE —
IT'S THE TRIKER!
HE STRIKES LIKE LIGHTNING — AND IS GONE. WHO WILL RID US OF THE TRIKER?

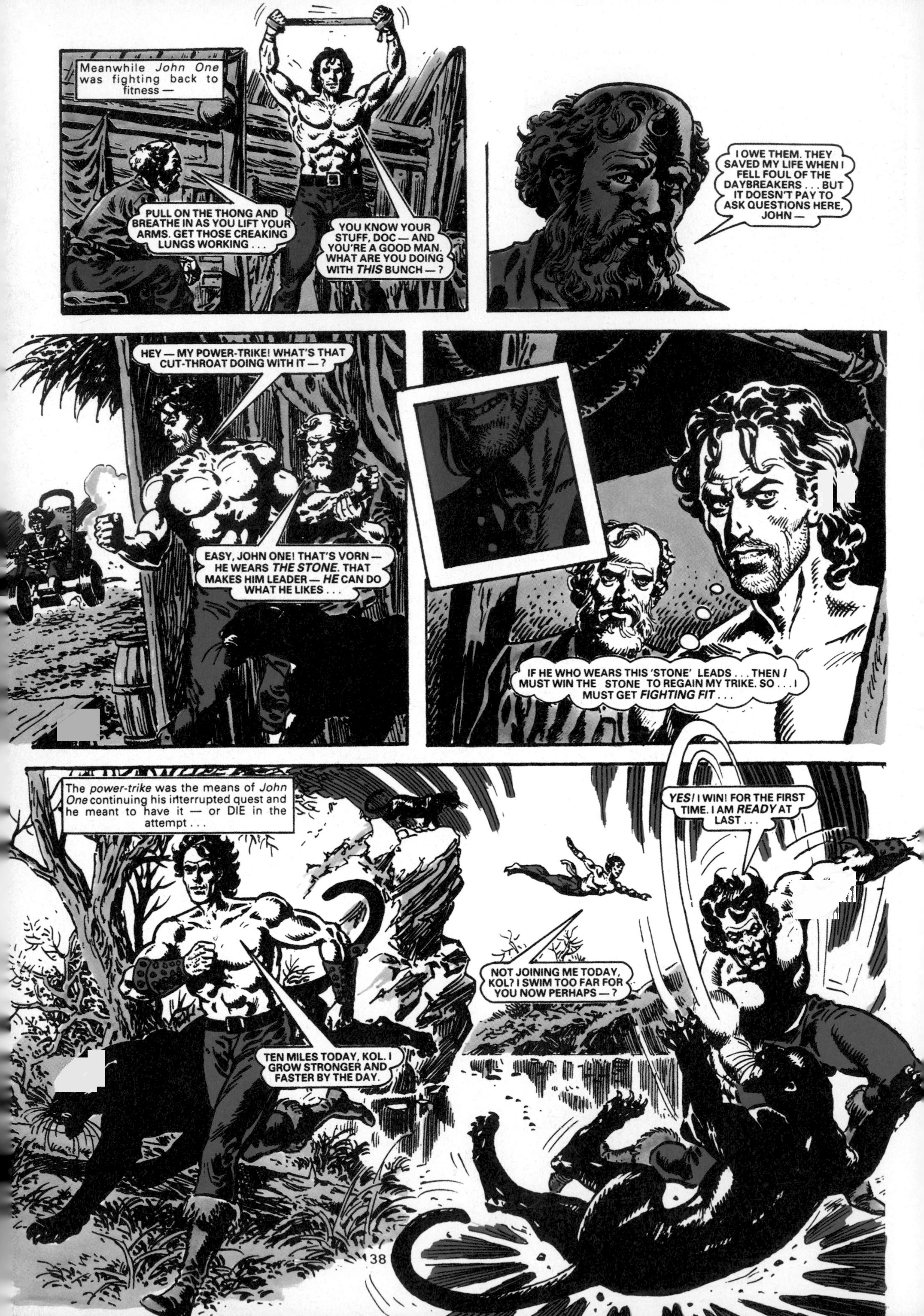

HEY — MY POWER-TRIKE! WHAT'S THAT CUT-THROAT DOING WITH IT — ?
EASY, JOHN ONE! THAT'S VORN — HE WEARS *THE STONE*. THAT MAKES HIM LEADER — *HE* CAN DO WHAT HE LIKES . . .

IF HE WHO WEARS THIS 'STONE' LEADS . . . THEN *I* MUST WIN THE STONE TO REGAIN MY TRIKE. SO . . . I MUST GET *FIGHTING FIT* . . .

The *power-trike* was the means of *John One* continuing his interrupted quest and he meant to have it — or DIE in the attempt . . .
TEN MILES TODAY, KOL. I GROW STRONGER AND FASTER BY THE DAY.
NOT JOINING ME TODAY, KOL? I SWIM TOO FAR FOR YOU NOW PERHAPS — ?
YES! I WIN! FOR THE FIRST TIME. I AM *READY* AT LAST . . .

Next day —
I DEMAND THE RIGHT TO FIGHT YOU FOR THE MACHINE, VORN. YOU AND I. THE CAT WILL NOT INTERFERE.
YOU'VE GOT GUTS, JOHN ONE — BUT I'LL SOON SPILL 'EM FOR YOU!
The Brig-Ones formed a circle around the fighters. There were no rules — and Vorn struck even as John One prepared for the action —
TOO SLOW OFF THE MARK, JOHN ONE. VORN WAITS FOR NO MAN —
UNGH!
AND NOW YOU DIE AND — AAGH! — MY ARM —
THIS TIME YOU'RE TOO SLOW, BRAGGARD —!
The fight swung this way and that . . .
VORN SHOULD HAVE FINISHED THE NEWCOMER BY NOW — HE HAS NOT EVEN DRAWN HIS DAGGER YET!
Vorn's power began to tell . . .
YOU'RE WEAKENING, JOHN ONE. I HAVE YOU NOW—
HE'S RIGHT. MY BODY LACKS RESERVES OF STRENGTH . . .
A last desperate burst of energy from John One —
GO FOR THE SOLAR PLEXUS . . . DRIVE THE BREATH FROM HIM . . . MY LAST CHANCE . . .
AAA-OWF!

CONTINUED ON PAGE 65.

THE DIVER

(A STORY OF THE FAMOUS REDS 'N' BLUES)

A word with twin strikers, Joe Johnson and Danny Kean —
YOU'VE HEARD ABOUT REDMOND COMING HERE? HE'LL HELP TAKE THE PRESSURE OFF YOU TWO! HE KNOWS WHERE THE GOAL IS!
LEAVE IT OUT, BOSS. ME AND DANNY HAVE BEEN SCORING!
NOT ENOUGH, THOUGH, JOE! I MEAN. . . THREE IN THE LAST SIX GAMES ISN'T NEARLY ENOUGH.
Col Redmond appeared ten minutes later —
HERE HE COMES, JOE. EVER PLAYED AGAINST HIM?
JUST THE ONCE, DANNY — BUT I WATCHED HIM PLAY A FEW YEARS BACK.
HOWDO, LADS! NICE TO BE WITH YOU . . .
IF HE GETS TOO MANY GOALS, DANNY, YOU AND ME COULD BECOME FLAMING REDUNDANT!
DON'T TALK DAFT, JOE. HE'LL GET A FEW GOALS ALL RIGHT. . . BUT HE'LL TAKE DEFENDERS OFF OUR BACKS! WHICH MEANS *WE'LL* SCORE MORE TOO!
I HOPE YOU'RE RIGHT, DANNY BOY. BUT SAM TORRIE'S GOT NO TIME FOR HIM, THAT'S FOR SURE!
AW, GO ON WITH YOU. DON'T TAKE ANY NOTICE OF WHAT SAM SAYS — HE'S THE WORLD'S BIGGEST MOANER!
Col ghosted past central defender Garry Fraser —
THAT'S CLASS! LOVELY BODY-SWERVE! GARRY HAD NO IDEA WHICH WAY HE WAS GOING . . .

Sam Torrie came powering in —
AAAAHHH!
I TOLD YOU, DIDN'T I? YOU SAW IT. . . THE DIVER AT WORK! HE ISN'T HURT. . . HE'S JUST DOING HIS STAGE-ACT!
RUBBISH, SAM! YOU WENT IN LIKE A MAD BULL! YOU TONE DOWN THE TACKLES. . . OR WE'RE GOING TO LOSE HALF OUR TEAM IN TRAINING SESSIONS!
HERE WE GO THEN, JOE — LET'S SHOW THEM THE TERRIBLE TWINS IN ACTION!
NO PROBLEM, DANNY BOY. WATCH ME FINISH THIS!
But —
HA! TOO EASY, CLEM!
C'MON, JOE. YOU'LL HAVE TO DO BETTER THAN THAT!

BETTER DO SOMETHING MYSELF. . . BEFORE THAT BIG BULL TORRIE KICKS ME OVER THE STAND AGAIN!
YOU'RE GOING NO PLACE, REDMOND.
TORRIE'S GOT IT IN FOR COL. HE'S DONE HIM AGAIN.
Redmond went down —
AW. . . HURT AGAIN, REDMOND? WHY DON'T YOU COMPLAIN TO THE MANAGER?
AND WHY DON'T YOU SHUT YOUR FAT TRAP, TORRIE?
Redmond was up in a flash. And —
HA! THAT BENT YOUR BACK, CLEM! MA-GIC, COL!
After training —
THIS IS MY CORNER, REDMOND! DON'T PUT YOUR STUFF HERE! I ALWAYS HAVE THE CORNER!
OKAY! SORRY! DIDN'T KNOW, DID I?
EASE OFF, SAM! YOU'RE GETTING OUT OF ORDER! GIVE THE GUY A CHANCE!
HE DOESN'T DESERVE A CHANCE, CLEM — HE'S A CREEP!
DON'T PAY ATTENTION TO TORRIE, COL! HE'S ALWAYS HAVING A GO!
IF HE WASN'T WINDING YOU UP. . . IT'D BE SOMEONE ELSE! FORGET HIM!

Later in the week, a practice match—
TAKE IT DOWN, WILLY. . . AND KNOCK IT OVER TO THE FAR POST. COL REDMOND'S MAKING A GOOD RUN!
The cross came over and up went Sam Torrie and Col Redmond—
AARRGGH! MY HEAD!
HERE WE GO AGAIN! GIVE HIM AN OSCAR, BOSS! DIVER REDMOND AT WORK!
NOT THIS TIME, SAM!
GET YOURSELF CLEANED UP AND LET DINGER BELL TAKE A LOOK AT IT! LOOKS LIKE IT NEEDS A COUPLE OF STITCHES.
I HOPE YOU DIDN'T DO THAT ON PURPOSE, SAM!
COURSE I DIDN'T! I MIGHT NOT LIKE THE GUY BUT I WOULDN'T CUT HIM UP LIKE THAT!
The following Saturday, Col Redmond made his first appearance for the Reds 'n' Blues against Leston Villa—
STICK IT WIDE, DANNY! I'M BEHIND YOU!
It wasn't an easy chance!
OOOHH... OFF THE BAR!

Fifteen minutes later —
GREAT DUMMY RUN! COL'S TAKEN HALF THE FLAMING DEFENCE WITH HIM!
The road to goal opened up for Danny Keen —
LEFT, JOE! SQUARE IT!
BE MY GUEST, DANNY BOY!
A good shot —
HIT THE POST! THE GOALIE GOT A TOUCH ON IT!
UNLUCKY, DANNY!
Col Redmond . . . reading the situation like a book —
YE-ES!
GREAT FOLLOWING UP, COL!
Early in the second half —
AAAHH!
REF! HOW ABOUT IT? THAT WAS A TRIP!
It wasn't only Sam Torrie who thought Col Redmond was a 'diver'!
PLAY ON. . . KEEP IT GOING!
YOU CAN FOOL SOME PEOPLE, REDMOND. BUT NOT ME!

The Reds 'n' Blues won their next three matches . . . but Col Redmond only scored one more goal
TRY ONE OF YOUR DIVES IN THE PENALTY BOX NEXT WEEK, REDMOND! IF YOU GET THE PENALTY. . . WE'LL LET YOU TAKE IT. JUST TO KEEP YOUR TALLY GOING!
GET OFF MY BACK, TORRIE! YOU'RE NOT FUNNY ANY MORE!
On Monday morning —
IT'S NOT WORKING OUT, BOSS! I'M NOT SCORING THE GOALS YOU EXPECTED FROM ME. AND I CAN'T STAND TORRIE ANY LONGER! I WANT OUT!
OH, COME ON, COL. YOU'RE NOT A QUITTER! TORRIE'S JUST A LOUD-MOUTH, WE ALL KNOW THAT!
I THOUGHT I COULD DO A JOB FOR THE REDS 'N' BLUES. . . EVEN IF IT WAS ONLY TO THE END OF THE SEASON. . . BUT IT'S GOING WRONG. . . TORRIE'S GOT EVERYBODY CALLING ME "THE DIVER". . . AND THE RESERVES RECKON I'M STEALING A FIRST-TEAM PLACE . . .
IT'S NOT GOING WRONG! WE'RE WINNING GAMES AGAIN. AND IT'S YOU THAT'S DOING IT FOR US.
I'D LIKE YOU TO KNOW I DIDN'T TAKE A DIVE IN THE CUP FINAL THREE YEARS BACK. I CAN PROVE IT TOO. LOOK AT THOSE PHOTOGRAPHS.
A PRESS PHOTOGRAPHER PAL OF MINE GAVE THEM TO ME. THEY WERE NEVER PUBLISHED. TORRIE BROUGHT ME DOWN! HE'S JUST NOT MAN ENOUGH TO ADMIT IT! I NEVER DIVED!
Ken kept the photos to show Sam Torrie —
I-I DUNNO, BOSS. . . I CAN'T REALLY REMEMBER. IT ALL HAPPENED SO FAST! LOOKS LIKE I DID GET A TOUCH ON HIM, THOUGH . . .
COL DOESN'T WANT ANYONE TO KNOW ABOUT THESE PHOTOS. JUST YOU, ME. . . AND HIM! SO LET'S FORGET THIS 'DIVING' EH?

Ken Robbins had a word with young John Gold, too!
IF YOU WERE READY FOR THE FIRST TEAM. . . I'D HAVE PLAYED YOU, JOHNNY! BUT YOU'RE NOT. . . YOU NEED ANOTHER SEASON IN THE RESERVES, UNDERSTAND?
YEAH. I GOTTA ADMIT I AIN'T HALF AS GOOD AS COL REDMOND. I MEAN, HE KNOWS IT ALL, DOESN'T HE! HE'S SOME PLAYER!
WE'RE DOING WELL IN THE F.A. CUP, COL. . . AND YOU'RE IN MY PLANS TO MAKE THE FINAL. WE CAN DO IT. WHAT DO YOU SAY?
MAXWEL
BONTONE
YOU'RE A GOOD BOSS, MISTER ROBBINS. YOU BELIEVE IN ME! OKAY, I'LL STAY . . .
With Sam Torrie off his back, Col began to turn on the style . . . taking the Reds 'n' Blues on a good Cup run —
OHHHHHH! WHAT A SHOT! COL REDMOND!
PONDIX
ROLESY
GO-AL!
The strike force of Joe Johnson, Danny Keen and Col Redmond took the Reds 'n' Blues all the way —
IT'S THERE! WE'RE IN THE FINAL!
THAT'S ALL HISTORY NOW OF COURSE. THAT HAPPENED LAST SEASON . . . AND YES . . . WE DID GO ON TO WIN THE CUP, BEATING SOUTHPOOL 2-1 IN THE FINAL. AND THE ONLY DIVE IN SIGHT WAS THE WINNING GOAL SCORED BY COL REDMOND . . . WITH A MAGNIFICENT DIVING HEADER!
AND ANOTHER THING COL BROUGHT US . . . WAS VERY VALUABLE TIME TO BRING ON YOUNG JOHN GOLD. AND JOHN IS NOW DOING VERY WELL FOR THE FIRST TEAM.
THE END

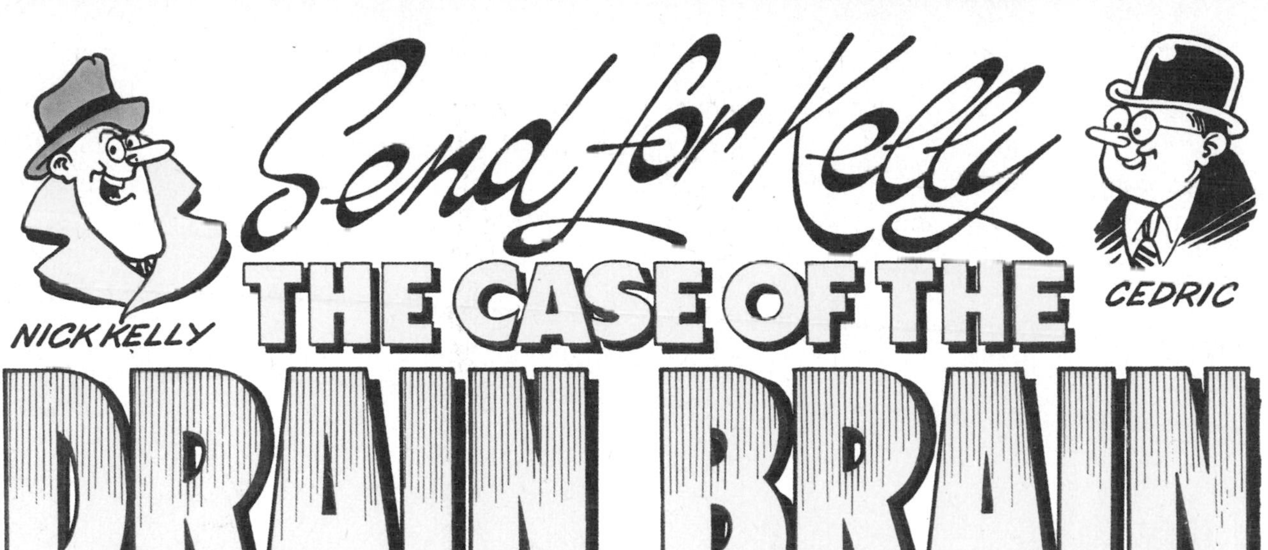
Send for Kelly
THE CASE OF THE
DRAIN BRAIN
NICK KELLY
CEDRIC

Top crimebusters Nick Kelly and his assistant, Cedric, paid a call on their old pal, the police chief . . .
POLICE CHIEF
KELLY, OLD CHAP, COME ON IN! OUR CRIME GRAPH'S DOWN, THANKS TO YOU.

SO IT IS, SIR! HA, HA, HA!
KLUNK!

THAT'S IT, LADS. GIVE KELLY A CRIME WAVE. IT'LL BE YOUR LAST. HO! HO!
CELLS

THE STREETS ARE SAFE PLACES TO BE NOW, CEDRIC, THANKS TO US.
YOU SAID IT, MR KELLY.

Meanwhile at Moneylot Mansion, Lord Toff was having a bath . . .

NEED YOUR HELP, KELLY! THERE'S BEEN A WHOLE SPATE OF ROBBERIES BY SOME FIEND FROM THE DRAINS!
THIS SMELLS NASTY, CHIEF.

MR KELLY!
WHAT IS IT, CEDRIC?
CHING!
RASP!
I'M DRAIN BRAIN! YOU CAN'T CATCH ME! RASP!

QUICKLY, CEDRIC! DOWN THAT MANHOLE!

PAWNBROKERS ARMS
FINE ALES
AFTER HIM . . . AAARGH!
DIVE!
THUD!

FINE ALES
WHAT YOU MIGHT CALL A TECHNICAL OUCH, CEDRIC!
THERE'S A MANHOLE, MR KELLY.

CAN'T SEE A THING, CEDRIC! STRIKE A MATCH!

YOW!
SORRY, MR KELLY.

DANGER
SEWER GAS
NO NAKED LIGHTS
THIS WAY, CEDRIC.

U.S. EMBASSY NO ADMITTANCE
RUSSIAN EMBASSY KEEP OUTSKI
SHHH. THOUGHT I HEARD SOMETHING, CEDRIC.
COULD IT BE DRAIN BRAIN?

RAT-TAT-TAT-TAT-TAT!
POW! POW! POW!
GET DOWN, CEDRIC!

DANGER
SEWER GAS
NO NAKED LIGHTS
THIS MEANS YOU
WHAT WAS ALL THAT ABOUT, MR KELLY?
WHAT THEY CALL SEWER POLITICS, CEDRIC.

LISTEN, CEDRIC, I HEAR MUSIC! DO YOU?
OUCH! WAIT TILL I STRIKE ANOTHER MATCH, MR KELLY.
BAKER STREET

AH, YES, I HEAR IT NOW, MR KELLY.
THE FACE SEEMS FAMILIAR. EXCUSE ME, SIR, HAVE YOU SEEN A BALDHEADED MAN WITH STARING EYES WHO CALLS HIMSELF DRAIN BRAIN?

PUSH OFF! CAN'T YOU SEE I'M ON A CASE?

THEY THINK THEY CAN CATCH ME. HE! HE! I'LL SHOW 'EM!
THE MALL
BILLINGSGATE FISH MARKET

THE MALL
THIS WAY, CEDRIC. IF I KNOW DRAIN BRAIN, HE'LL GO AFTER RICH PICKINGS.
DANGER SEWER GAS NO NAKED LIGHTS
COR! SOME PEOPLE ASK FOR TROUBLE!
WE'RE NEARLY OUT OF MATCHES, MR KELLY.

WONDER WHERE THAT LEADS TO, MR KELLY?
SNIFF. SNIFF. I DETECT THE FAINT BUT UNMISTAKABLE AROMA OF THE SEA, CEDRIC.

WHOOOOOSH!

DANGER SEWER GAS NO NAKED LIGHTS ARE THEY THICK- OR WHAT?
I GUESS THE TIDE JUST CAME IN, MR KELLY.
DON'T BE STUPID, CEDRIC. LET'S MOVE ON!

LISTEN, CEDRIC. FOOTSTEPS!
IT MUST BE DRAIN BRAIN, MR KELLY!

DOOMTOWN RATS IN CONCERT
FALSE ALARM, CEDRIC.

THESE SUPERSNOOPS ARE GETTING TOO CLOSE TO MY HIDEOUT, SNAPPER. YOU WILL SEE THEM OFF.

AFTER 'EM, BOY!
DANGER SEWER GAS NO NAKED LIGHTS
OOOH! THERE'S JUST NO USE TALKING TO SOME FOLKS!

MY LEGS ACHE, MR KELLY. WE MUST HAVE WALKED FOR MILES.
HERE'S A CONVENIENT LOG, CEDRIC. CLIMB ABOARD.

I ONCE SAW A FILM ABOUT AN ALLIGATOR THAT LIVED DOWN A SEWER, MR KELLY. IT ATE EVERYBODY IN SIGHT.
FAR-FETCHED RUBBISH, CEDRIC. THESE FILM-MAKERS EXPECT YOU TO BELIEVE ANYTHING!

YIPES!
YOU WERE SAYING, MR KELLY?

DID YOU SAY THAT ALLIGATOR IN THE FILM ATE EVERYBODY, CEDRIC?
EVERYBODY, MR KELLY! YE-E-EOOOW!
RRRIP!

JUMP, CEDRIC!
VICTORIA
STATION
FALLS

DO YOU THINK THIS COULD BE WHAT WE'RE LOOKING FOR, MR KELLY?
COULD BE, CEDRIC. STAND ASIDE WHILE I PICK THE LOCK.
DRAIN BRAIN'S TOP SECRET HIDEOUT
NO HAWKERS
TRADESMEN'S ENTRANCE ROUND THE BACK

THAT'S NOT QUITE WHAT I THOUGHT YOU MEANT, MR KELLY.
NOW TRY IT, CEDRIC.
DRAIN BR SECRET
WHACK!
TOOLCHEST

THE GAME IS UP, DRAIN BRAIN! YOU HAVE BEEN SCUPPERED BY A SUPERIOR MIND!
YOU THINK SO, KELLY?

YOU'LL NEVER CATCH ME ON MY TRUSTY DRAINING BOARD! HA, HA, HA!
VRRRROOM!

WHAT NOW, MR KELLY? DRAIN BRAIN'S GOT CLEAN AWAY. OUCH! AND WE'RE DOWN TO OUR LAST MATCH.
PICCADILLY CIRCUS
I'VE AN IDEA, CEDRIC. WE MUST GO UP TOP.

DANGER SEWER GAS NO NAKED LIGHTS OH, WELL— DON'T SAY YOU HAVEN'T BEEN WARNED!
THAT'S TORN IT. THE LADDER'S BROKEN. NOW HOW DO WE REACH THE STREET?

BOOOOM!

EXCUSE ME, MY MAN. I'D LIKE YOU TO DANCE. . .
PICCADILLY CIRCUS HEAP GOOD SHOW NOW BOOKING
HOW!

NO, YOU DON'T UNDERSTAND. NOT THE TANGO. I WANT YOU TO DO A RAIN DANCE.

OOOWALLA! OOOWALLA! OOCHI-COO!
HOLD IT! I WANT RAIN — NOT SNOW!

SORRY! HAVEN'T DONE THIS FOR AGES. NOW HOW IT GO?

RAINDROPS KEEP FALLING ON MY HEAD! OOCHI-COO — OOO-OOO!
IT'S STARTING TO RAIN, MR KELLY.

HOW DOES THIS GRAB YOU, DRAIN BRAIN?
IT'S A RAGING TORRENT DOWN THERE, MR KELLY!

WHOOSH!
THERE HE IS, CEDRIC!

And later . . .
WE'VE A SPECIAL CELL FOR YOU, DRAIN BRAIN. YOU SHOULD FEEL AT HOME IN HERE.
CELLS
A JOB WELL DONE, EH, MR KELLY? I FEEL FLUSHED WITH SUCCESS.
OUCH! REALLY, CEDRIC!
THE END

SECRETS OF THE SPIES

SECRET AGENTS IN GERMAN-OCCUPIED EUROPE RAN THE CONSTANT RISK OF BEING STOPPED AND SEARCHED. TO CARRY A GUN OR MORE OBVIOUS WEAPON COULD MEAN INSTANT DEATH. THESE WEAPONS AND OTHER DEVICES WERE DEVELOPED TO MAKE THE AGENTS LIFE MORE SECURE.

This crossbow could fire its dart some 200 yards. This made it an ideal weapon for eliminating enemy sentries.

This ingenious heel-plate for a boot or shoe concealed two sharp blades. These could be used by an agent to cut himself free if he were caught and tied up.

This fist gun was attached to a strong leather glove. Used at close quarters, it fired a single .38 bullet when the wearer punched his adversary with his clenched fist.

This "fountain pen" could be used to fire a small needle dart 40 feet. The needle could be tipped with a poison if required.

With Germans determined to track down the secret agents' vital radio communications, it was necessary to move the radio sets frequently. This everyday suitcase in fact concealed a powerful radio set.

KING COBRA
Freelance reporter Bill King was with a party of newsmen drawn to a remote area of India by the rumour of the revival of an old killer cult . . .
MISTER THILAK, THIS IS AN ELEGANT VEHICLE FOR AN HOTEL BUS.
KING-SAHIB, THIS LIMOUSINE IS LEFT OVER FROM THE WEALTHY TIMES BEFORE THE NOBLE ASHOKA FAMILY TURN THEIR PALACE INTO HOTEL.
HEY, THILAK, WHAT CAN YOU TELL US ABOUT THIS COBRA GANG THAT'S BEEN RANSOMING LOCAL BUSINESSMEN?
TUTTLE-SAHIB, HUMBLE PERSON LIKE MYSELF IS NOT KNOWING OF SUCH MATTERS.
ODD THAT SOMEBODY WHO KNOWS NOTHING SHOULD HAVE A COBRA TATTOOED ON HIS ARM.

GENTLEMEN, WELCOME TO MY HOTEL. I AM TOMMY ASHOKA.
PRINCE ASHOKA, I RECKON YOU KNOW WHY WE'RE ALL HERE. IS IT TRUE YOU'VE BEEN THREATENED BY THE COBRA GANG?
OLD BOY, YONDER IN THE JUNGLE ARE THE RUINS OF A SHRINE ONCE USED BY A MURDER SECT WHICH SOME RASCALS ARE NOW TRYING TO REVIVE. I ASSURE YOU THEY WOULDN'T DARE TRY ANYTHING AGAINST ONE OF MY FAMILY.
NOW FORGET SUCH DISAGREEABLE MATTERS AND ENJOY A DISPLAY OF KALARIPAYIT. THESE MARTIAL ARTS WERE KNOWN TO US INDIANS LONG BEFORE SUCH SKILLS BEGAN IN CHINA AND JAPAN.
THE SPING-SWORD. A MAN'S HEAD CAN BE TAKEN OFF WITH ONE OF THOSE. THE OTHER CHAP DEFENDS HIMSELF WITH A PAIR OF KATAR DAGGERS.
MATE, I'M STARTING TO THINK THERE'S NO STORY! COULD JUST BE A PUBLICITY STUNT FOR THE HOTEL!
COULD BE — BUT THERE HAS BEEN ONE DEFINITE MURDER AND THERE MAY BE KIDNAPPINGS THE VICTIMS HAVE BEEN TOO FRIGHTENED TO REPORT.
That night . . .
JUST A QUICK CHECK UP ON THE DETAILS. MADRAS BUSINESSMAN SNATCHED BY MEN IN SNAKE-HEAD MASKS WHILE HOLIDAYING AT HIS COUNTRY ESTATE. HIS FAMILY WERE ADVISED BY THE POLICE NOT TO PAY RANSOM AND THE MAN WAS FOUND DEAD, INJECTED WITH COBRA VENOM.
A SHOT! WHAT'S GOING ON?
BANG

THE PRINCE! HE'S BEEN TAKEN!
Bill became his other self — King Cobra!
STRANGE THIS KILLER GANG SHOULD ALSO BE ASSOCIATED WITH COBRAS. STILL, THE COBRA CULT EXISTED IN INDIA LONG BEFORE ME.
FRESH TRACKS ARE EASY TO FOLLOW WITH MY INFRA-RED RAY.
THAT MUST BE THE ANCIENT SHRINE SPOKEN OF BY TOMMY.
THE TRACKS LEAD INSIDE.
King Cobra's power-grip gloves bore him up the temple wall . . .

THERE'S TOMMY. NO SIGN OF HIS CAPTORS.
King Cobra used his flying-squirrel membrane . . .
HE SEEMS UNCONSCIOUS — DRUGGED PERHAPS!
A TRAP-DOOR! I'VE FALLEN INTO A TRAP!
NO ROOM TO SPREAD MY SQUIRREL RIG.
SNAKES....COBRAS! I HAD BETTER KEEP VERY STILL.

HAW! HAW! YOU WERE EXPECTED! I KNEW THE BAIT WOULD BRING YOU TO MY TRAP!
I AM THE TRUE LORD OF THE COBRA. THERE IS NO PLACE FOR A FALSE KING. IN THE PIT SHALL YOU PERISH ON THE FANGS OF MY SERPENT FOLLOWERS.
A TRAP TO GET RID OF ME?! I SHOULD FEEL FLATTERED.
I'VE GOT TO STAY PERFECTLY STILL AND THINK THIS THROUGH!
A FLUTE! THAT DOOR WASN'T OPEN BEFORE.
THE SNAKES ARE ENTRANCED BY RHYTHM. I'M SAFE AS LONG AS I MOVE SLOWLY.

I'M CLEAR BUT THE FLUTE-PLAYER HAS GONE. I APPEAR TO HAVE A MYSTERIOUS FRIEND.
MORE MUSIC! DRUMMING THIS TIME!
SO YOU LIVE, FALSE KING! IT MAY BE YOU DO KNOW A LITTLE OF THE WAYS OF THE COBRA.
BUT NOW YOU FACE THE KATAR DAGGERS IN THE GRIP OF AN EXPERT.
IT IS BETTER YOU DIE BY MY OWN HAND.
YOU MAY BE IN FOR A SHOCK!
ARGH!
MY GLOVES CAN BE CHARGED WITH ELECTRICTY!

KILL HIM! KILL THE FALSE COBRA KING!
AAAGH! THE TRAP-DOOR!
MISTER THILAK THE CHAUFFEUR!
GET YOU GONE! YOUR TIMES OF MURDER ARE ENDED! RUN BEFORE THE POLICE COME LOOKING FOR YOU!
FORGIVE HIM, KING COBRA. HE THOUGHT TO BRING BACK THE EVIL OLD WAYS TO CLEAR HEAVY DEBTS.
WHAT? YOU MEAN IT WAS . . .
MY MASTER — THE PRINCE ASHOKA! BETTER HE LIES DEAD THAN LIVES TO FURTHER DISGRACE HIS NOBLE FAMILY.
THE COBRA CULT HAS BEEN DORMANT THESE MANY YEARS. THE ASHOKA FAMILY WERE ALWAYS OUR LEADERS AND INITIATED IN OUR WAYS,BUT HE SOUGHT TO GAIN WEALTH FROM US. HE WAS WARNED BUT REFUSED TO LISTEN — SO HE HAD TO DIE.
Next day . . .
THILAK, WHY ARE WE BEING KICKED OUT? WHY CAN'T I SPEAK TO HIS NIBS?
SO SORRY, TUTTLE-SAHIB, BUT PRINCE ASHOKA IS OCCUPIED WITH THE SAD AFFAIR OF A FUNERAL.
The End

CONTINUED FROM PAGE 40.

Hunted

CHAPTER THREE

E

The youngsters crept closer—
HE'S ALONE! I SAY WE TAKE HIM ON — NOW-!
NO! HE'S A KILLER, AND—
FAINT-HEARTED TYPICAL FEMALE! TELLAN'S RIGHT— THIS IS OUR CHANCE . . .
I'LL STUN HIM WITH THIS ROCK. BE READY TO MOVE IN — !
But John One's hearing, honed for survival, had picked up the sound of the newcomers' approach . . . and his reaction was fast and frightening!
I COULD JUST AS EASILY HAVE PUT THAT THROUGH YOUR NECK, BOY . . .
WELL YOU'LL HAVE TO PUT THE NEXT ONE THROUGH MY NECK THEN. IT'S ALL THAT WILL STOP ME KILLING YOU— MURDERING BRIG!
I AM NO BRIG NOR A MURDERER, YOUNGSTER—
LIAR! WE HAVE ALL SEEN YOUR TRIKE LEADING RAIDS ON THE SETTLEMENTS!
THROW DOWN YOUR BOW AND LET ME AVENGE MY BROTHER'S DEATH—
HOLD FAST, BOY — OR YOUR MOTHER WILL BE MOURNING THE DEATH OF ANOTHER SON . . .
YOU DON'T FRIGHTEN ME, BRIG!

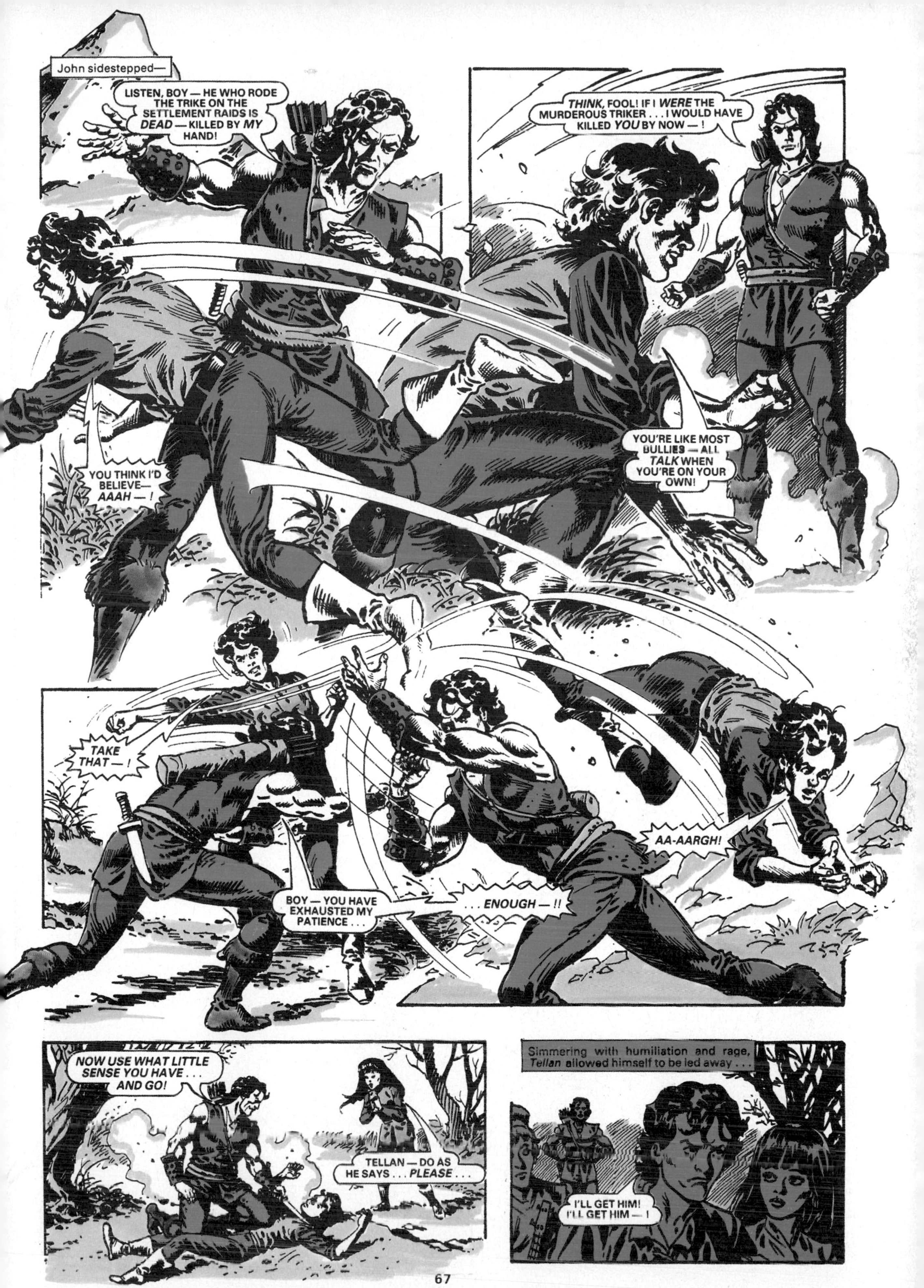

John sidestepped—

LISTEN, BOY — HE WHO RODE THE TRIKE ON THE SETTLEMENT RAIDS IS *DEAD* — KILLED BY *MY* HAND!

YOU THINK I'D BELIEVE— *AAAH* — !

THINK, FOOL! IF I *WERE* THE MURDEROUS TRIKER . . . I WOULD HAVE KILLED *YOU* BY NOW — !

YOU'RE LIKE MOST BULLIES — ALL *TALK* WHEN YOU'RE ON YOUR OWN!

TAKE THAT — !

BOY — YOU HAVE EXHAUSTED MY PATIENCE . . .

. . . *ENOUGH* — !!

AA-AARGH!

When the youngsters had gone—
FOOD! WELL DONE, KOL. AT LEAST WE WILL CARRY OUT OUR MISSION ON FULL BELLIES . . .
But in a nearby Settlement, Tellan was stirring up trouble for John One—
. . . I DON'T CARE WHAT HE SAYS — HE IS THE TRIKER! I'M SURE OF IT. THERE WILL NEVER BE A BETTER CHANCE TO NAIL HIM, FATHER—
YOU'RE RIGHT, SON — I'LL ORGANISE SOME OF THE SETTLERS!
And while John One set out towards the Techno-Cemetery, the Settlers were on their way . . .
USE THAT NOSE OF YOURS TO SNIFF OUT THE MINES, KOL — I'LL FOLLOW.
THERE HE IS. TAD — GO RIGHT WITH YOUR GROUP. LARP — GO LEFT . . .
KOL AVOIDS THE MINES AS IF BY MAGIC. WE'LL BE IN AND OUT AGAIN WITHOUT THE GUARDS KNOWING . . .
A TWIG CRACKED! — ! BEHIND ME. YET KOL IS AHEAD—
TIME TO PAY FOR YOUR CRIMES, TRIKER —IN BLOOD!
YOU AGAIN — ! ARE YOU ALL OUT OF YOUR MINDS, BLUNDERING IN HERE — ? THIS IS A MINEFIELD — !

The Settlers hesitated—
HOW THEN CAN YOU WALK SAFELY THROUGH IT?
SIMPLE . . . HE SNIFFS THE MINES OUT AND I FOLLOW . . .

A MANEATER! FLEE!
NO! DON'T RUN — ! THE MINES! YOU'LL—

OH, NO — THE POOR FOOLS — !
BOOM

The sound of mine explosions was heard by the Techno-Cemetery guards and suddenly the whole area was alive with light and gunfire!
WHEEEEEEEEE
NOTHING WE CAN DO TO HELP, KOL — BUT WE MUST USE THE DISTRACTION TO CARRY OUT OUR TASK—
AA-AIEE!

Within seconds John One and Kol were over the perimeter fence and inside the compound. While Kol stood guard, his master set to work—
AH — THIS IS WHAT I SEEK. IT IS A VERY SMALL PART . . . BUT IT WILL TAKE A MINUTE OR TWO TO DISCONNECT IT . . .

But as Kol prowled . . . watching, listening . . . he disturbed a finely balanced pile of scrap—
CRASH
OH, NO! THE GUARDS ARE BOUND TO HEAR THAT RACKET— WHATEVER IT WAS! THEY'LL COME RUNNING. KOL— COME, BOY. WE MUST HIDE. KOL — !
John One wasted precious seconds looking for his faithful companion — and paid the price!
HOLD IT RIGHT THERE, BRIG — AND DON'T GO FOR YOUR WEAPON—
MANACLE HIM AND TAKE HIM TO THE COMMANDER!
In the Commander's office—
THE PENALTY FOR BREAKING INTO A TECHNO-CEMETERY IS DEATH. WHAT DO YOU HAVE TO SAY FOR YOURSELF?
TH-THAT PHOTOGRAPH ON THE WALL — IT'S MATHOR — MY FATHER —!
THAT'S A PASS — HE'S BEEN HERE. AND NOW HE'LL BE AT EITHER ELECTRIC CITY OR QUO-POWER 8!
10·4·20
Teacher MATHOR
CLEARED FOR VISIT TO TECH-CHEM 31 THEN TO ELEC CITY AND QUO-POWER 8
SIGNED
The Commander's harsh voice cut in on John One's thoughts—
NOTHING TO SAY, EH? TAKE HIM AWAY AND TOSS HIM INTO THE CRUSHER—

As *John One* was led away to his fate, his mind churning, *Kol* was making another bid to escape from the hulk that had entrapped him—
I CAN'T DIE NOW I'M SO CLOSE TO FINDING MY FATHER.
IF ONLY KOL WERE HERE . . .
MEET THE CRUSHER, SCUM — IT'LL CHEW YOU UP AND SPIT YOU OUT IN LITTLE PIECES.
GOT TO MAKE A BREAK FOR IT. IT'S NOW OR NEVER . . .
There came a sudden sound of shattering glass . . .
CRASH
. . . and *Kol* was free — a black fury streaking to the rescue of his master — !
AARGH! WHAT IS IT —?
NO — GET BACK— AAI-EE —!
KOL! MY FRIEND, I AM GLAD TO SEE YOU . . .
John One was quick to take advantage of the guards' shock—
NOW LET'S SEE HOW *YOU* LIKE THE CRUSHER, PIG—
AA-EE-ARGH! NO-O-O . . .

CONTINUED ON PAGE 97.

ODD GUNS

Many strange guns have been used over the years. Here is our artist's views on some of them.
THE KNIFE GUN — A combination of a knife and a gun, it only fired a small calibre bullet, but was deadly at close quarters.
THE KEY GUN — This weird gun was used by jailers in British prisons many years ago. It opened the locks and also protected the jailers.
AH-TISHOO!
PARP!
THE PEPPER-BOX GUN — One of the first multi-shot pistols, this gun was popular in the 19th century. It had a number of revolving barrels, each of which fired a single shot.
THE SWORD GUN — An ingenious weapon of the 16th century was this Spanish-made sword, which had a small double-barrelled pistol built into it.
THE BATTLE-AXE GUN — One of the strangest combined weapons was this German flintlock pistol and battle-axe, used in the 17th century.
THE MOB GUN — A four-barrelled flintlock pistol, the Mob Gun was used in Britain in the 19th century. All four barrels fired at once.

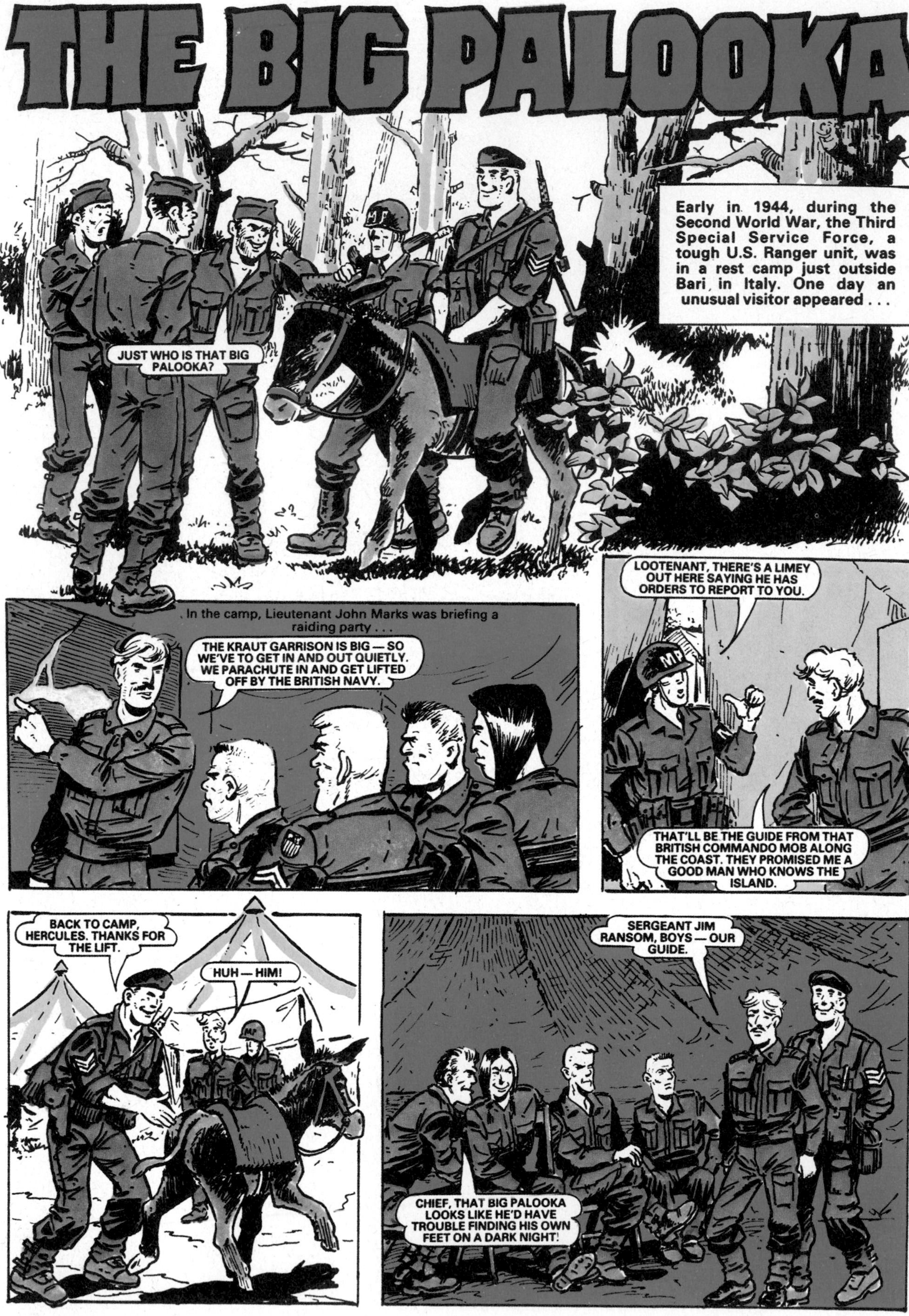

THE BIG PALOOKA

Early in 1944, during the Second World War, the Third Special Service Force, a tough U.S. Ranger unit, was in a rest camp just outside Bari, in Italy. One day an unusual visitor appeared . . .

JUST WHO IS THAT BIG PALOOKA?

. In the camp, Lieutenant John Marks was briefing a raiding party . . .

THE KRAUT GARRISON IS BIG — SO WE'VE TO GET IN AND OUT QUIETLY. WE PARACHUTE IN AND GET LIFTED OFF BY THE BRITISH NAVY.

LOOTENANT, THERE'S A LIMEY OUT HERE SAYING HE HAS ORDERS TO REPORT TO YOU.

THAT'LL BE THE GUIDE FROM THAT BRITISH COMMANDO MOB ALONG THE COAST. THEY PROMISED ME A GOOD MAN WHO KNOWS THE ISLAND.

RIGHT, BOYS! OUR TARGET IS THE ISLE OF KARJE. OUR MISSION TO LOCATE ONE CRASHED COURIER PLANE AND SALVAGE DOCUMENTS CONTAINING TOP-SECRET INFORMATION ON OUR CONTACTS WITH THE YUGOSLAV PARTISANS.

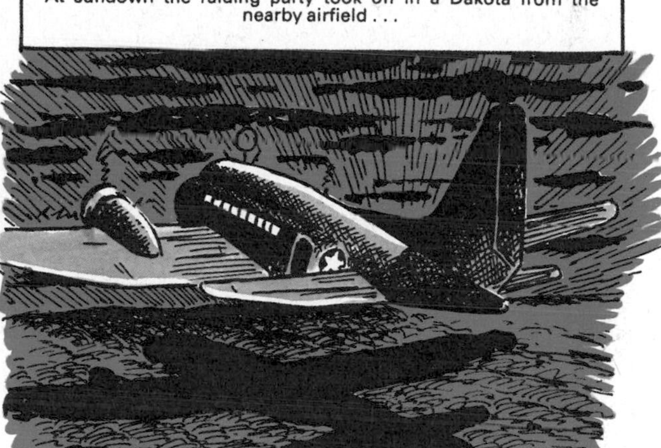
At sundown the raiding party took off in a Dakota from the nearby airfield . . .

THIS AIR RECCE PICTURE SHOWS THE PILOT MANAGED TO GET THE PLANE DOWN IN ONE PIECE ON THE LAKE. WHAT ARE THE CHANCES OF THE KRAUTS HAVING GOT TO IT?
SIR, IT'S ROUGH COUNTRY AND JERRY MOSTLY STICKS TO THE COAST. WE MAY BE LUCKY.

SIR, BEG PARDON, BUT I SHOULD BRIEF OUR AIRCREW WHERE TO DUMP US. IT'S BOGGY BY THE LAKE, BUT THERE'S SOME EASY GROUND A HALF MILE OFF.
GO AHEAD. THAT'S WHAT YOU'RE HERE FOR.

Over the island . . .
RANDOM'S GONE! WE'D BEST GET AFTER HIM!

The raiders came to earth . . .
ARGH!

YOUR NOTION OF A GOOD LANDING SPOT DIDN'T DO THE LOOTENANT MUCH GOOD, LIMEY!
AT LEAST THE REST OF US GOT DOWN ALL RIGHT.

PROBABLY CONCUSSED FROM THE CRACK ON THE HEAD. I'LL SPLINT THE BROKEN LEG WHILE YOU FELLOWS FASHION A STRETCHER.
NOW, HOLD ON WITH THE ORDERS, YOU BIG PALOOKA. CORPORAL BOGAN TAKES OVER NOW THE LOOTENANT IS OUT OF ACTION.

ACTUALLY, BLOKES, I AM NOW IN COMMAND AS SENIOR SOLDIER.
THE BIG PALOOKA'S RIGHT! ANYWAY, WE AIN'T LEAVING THE LOOTENANT — SO LET'S MAKE THAT STRETCHER.

As dawn broke . . .

THERE IT IS — ONE LIMEY LYSANDER AIRPLANE. WE GOT TO GET OUT TO IT.
I AGREE, BUT ONLY AFTER WE HAVE DISPOSED OF THE GUARD POSTED ON IT.

Jim prowled and then . . .

The guard was distracted . . .
ACH — WAS IST . . .

GUTEN MORGEN, FRITZ. I SPEAK A LITTLE GERMAN,IF YOU'D CARE TO TELL ME THINGS.

THIS LAD SAYS THE PILOT WAS KILLED IN THE CRASH. HIS BODY,ALONG WITH STUFF FOUND IN THE AIRCRAFT,WAS TAKEN TO THE GARRISON.
WHICH MEANS THE KRAUTS HAVE GOT THOSE PAPERS.
LIMEY, I HOPE YOU AIN'T THINKING OF US FOUR TAKING ON TWO HUNDRED KRAUTS!
NOW YOU MENTION IT,I SUPPOSE THE ODDS DO SEEM A BIT UNEVEN.

CORPORAL, I SUGGEST YOU STAY HERE WITH THE STRETCHER WHILE I TAKE ONE OF YOUR CHAPS ON A SNOOP —
HOLD IT RIGHT THERE, YOU BIG PALOOKA! YOU MAY THINK YOU'RE IN COMMAND, BUT I'M NOT RISKING MY GUYS IN ANY CRAZY SCHEME!

CORPORAL BOGAN, IS THERE NO WAY I CAN PERSUADE YOU TO AT LEAST LISTEN?
SHUCKS, I'M NOT UNREASONABLE WITH A CHIV AT MY GULLET! JUST TALK AWAY, LIMEY.

Jim did some persuading . . .
IT'S CRAZY, SURE ENOUGH — BUT YOU'VE WORE ME OUT, LIMEY. GO AHEAD WITH THE CHIEF WHILE WE TAKE OUR CHANCE WITH THE STRETCHER.

THE FUEL DUMP — JUST WHAT WE NEED FOR A DIVERSION.

A FEW DABS OP PLASTIC EXPLOSIVE AND A TIME PENCIL SET FOR A SHORT DELAY.

NOW FOR THE OFFICE OF THE GARRISON COMMANDANT. THE FUEL DUMP SHOULD GO UP ANY SECOND NOW . . .

ACHTUNG! FEUER!

RIGHT, CHIEF — OPEN UP.

BE STILL AND QUIET! WHERE IS THE BLACK CASE TAKEN FROM THE AIRCRAFT THAT CRASHED?
THE SAFE — ER, BUT ONLY THE MAJOR HAS THE KEY AND HE IS NOT HERE.

I'M GOING TO TRY BLOWING IT. BETTER DUCK DOWN AWAY FROM ANY WINDOWS.

Another explosion shook the port . . .
ACHTUNG! THE COMMANDANT'S OFFICE!

BY GOLLY, YOU BIG PALOOKA, YOU DONE IT!
BUT NOISILY — TOO MUCH EXPLOSIVE. YOU TAKE THE CASE AND WE'LL GO.

THEY'VE SPOTTED US! KEEP GOING, CHIEF!
AHHHHHHHHHH!

THERE COME THE STRETCHER PARTY.
GIVE THEM COVER.

THERE'S A LAUNCH TIED UP ON THE JETTY.
LET'S HOPE IT'S GASSED UP.

URGH — WHERE AM I? WHAT'S GOING ON?
LOOTENANT, GO BACK TO SLEEP! THIS AIN'T A GOOD TIME TO WAKE UP!

OH, NO, YOU DON'T, MATE!

CAST OFF THOSE LINES WHILE I START THE ENGINE.

The raiders departed . . .
ODD YOU BLOKES CALLING ME A BIG PALOOKA. THAT'S WHAT I WAS NAMED BY SOME YANK RANGERS I ONCE TRAINED, BUT I GOT QUITE FRIENDLY WITH THEM IN THE END.
I CAN BELIEVE THAT! YOU SORT OF GROW ON FOLKS!
THE END

KING COBRA
MORGAN'S
SERVICE STATION
After completing an assignment for a national English newspaper in America, ace reporter Bill King took a holiday in Alabama. One day he stopped in the little town of Marshville . . .
COFFEE
TOBACCO
OIL
HEY, YOU SERVE US FIRST, OLE MAN!
GET LOST, JOSH! YOU DEANS ALWAYS WUZ BULLYIN' COYOTES — LIKE YOUR PAPPY AFORE YOU.

F

NOBODY CALLS US DEANS COYOTES, OLE MAN.

NOW, PLEASE, DON'T FIGHT ON MY ACCOUNT. YOU'RE PERFECTLY WELCOME TO . . .
OUTA MY WAY, MAN.
BLAAAM
STAY WHAR Y'ARE, JOSH DEANS! LEAVE GRAMPS ALONE!
HOLY CROW!

GIT, I SAY!
NOW, BOBBY, THAT WAREN'T TOO FRIENDLY!
SUPER
LET'S GO, JOSH. WE'LL GET OUR GAS ELSEWHERE.

HOODLUMS! GOT TOO BIG FOR THAR BRITCHES EVER SINCE MANFRED WATERMAN TOOK OVER THE BIG HOUSE AN' EMPLOYED 'EM.
MANFRED WATERMAN?
HE'S A BIGWIG FROM NEW YORK. GOT BODYGUARDS WITH HIM. LOTS OF PEOPLE BIN SELLIN' PROPERTY TO HIM.

But King sensed a news story . . .
IF YOU'RE GONNA STAY, MISTER, WE RENT A ROOM.
NO THANKS, SON. THOSE DEAN BOYS MIGHT BE BACK. I'LL FIND A PLACE IN TOWN.

BIT LILY-LIVERED, AIN'T HE, GRAMPS?
WELL, HE AIN'T GOT YOUR SPUNK, BOBBY, THAT'S FOR SURE.

That night . . .
THAT OLE MAN'S GONNA BE MIGHTY SORRY, BROTHER TOM.
YOU BET, JOSH!
K . . . KING COBRA!
SPHLUUUT
NOW TO DEAL WITH YOU BULLIES!
AAAAH!
YOU NEXT!
URGH!
SPARE ME . . . AAAAAH!
G . . . GOLLY, GRAMPS, LOOK!
WHAT DO YOU KNOW ABOUT THIS WATERMAN GUY?
HE . . . HE USES US AND HIS MOB TO FRIGHTEN FOLKS INTO SELLIN' ANY PROPERTY HE WANTS. THAT'S HOW HE GOT THE POOL HALL, A COUPLA STORES AN' THE DIXIE HOTEL. FOLKS ARE TOO SCARED TO TELL!
OKAY, YOU CAN GO. BUT IF YOU BOTHER GRAMPS MORGAN AND BOBBY AGAIN, YOU'RE IN BIG TROUBLE.
OUFF! WE WON'T!

King Cobra headed for Bill King's room at the Rest-U Hotel. Bill and the ace crook catcher were one and the same.
I'M GLAD I DECIDED TO STAY. IT'S TIME SOMEONE DEALT WITH MR WATERMAN.
Next morning . . .
NEWSDESK? LOOK, I'M ON TO A STORY! WHAT DO YOU KNOW ABOUT A MANFRED WATERMAN?
HEY, YOU CUT ME OFF!
THAT'S RIGHT, MISTER. I WANT NO TROUBLE WITH MR WATERMAN. NOW YOU JUST PAY YOUR BILL — AND GIT!
YOU CAN PUT ME UP, MR MORGAN? THE HOTELS IN TOWN AIN'T TOO KEEN ON REPORTERS.
YEH, YUH'LL BE SAFE HERE NOW, MISTER. KING COBRA'S KEEPIN' AN EYE ON US!
YEH, WE ACTUALLY SAW HIM!
Meanwhile . . .
COBRA . . . AND NOW A REPORTER! WHAT'S GOIN' ON?
DUNNO, BOSS! THE WOMAN IN THE REST-U HOTEL HEARD HIM CALLIN' NEW YORK! HE MENTIONED YOUR NAME.
I WANT THAT REPORTER GUY RUBBED OUT. OKAY, GARRONI?
YES, MR VASS . . . I MEAN WATERMAN.
At ten to three . . .
I WANT YOU TO TELEPHONE MR BABBIT, THE BARBER BOBBY. TELL HIM HIS HOUSE IS ON FIRE. IT'S IMPORTANT THAT YOU PHONE AT EXACTLY THREE O'CLOCK!
G . . . GEE . . . OKAY. I'LL DISGUISE MA VOICE. THIS'LL GO TOWARD A NEW FISHIN' ROD. SURE HOPE GRAMPS DOESN'T FIND OUT THOUGH!

HE'S GOIN' INTO THE BARBER'S.
THERE'S A COUPLE A CUSTOMERS IN THERE. WE'D BEST WAIT A BIT.
Three o'clock . . .
EXCUSE ME, GENTLEMEN!
BRRUNG BRRUNG
FIRE! FIRE! AH, GOTTA GO! MA HOUSE IS ON FIRE!
DANG ME, AHM COMIN' TOO, WALT! AIN'T BEEN TO A GOOD BLAZE IN AGES!
WE GOT IT ON A PLATE!
YOU SHOULDA GIVEN THE POOR GINK TIME TO SAY HIS PRAYERS, GARRONI!
NOW YOU'D BETTER SAY YOURS, GARRONI!
K . . . K . . . KING COBRA!
AAAANGH!
YOU WASTED LEAD, FRIEND! NOT ONLY AM I PROTECTED FROM BULLETS BY MY SKIN BUT MY SPECIAL GAUNTLETS DEFLECT THEM EXACTLY AS I WISH!

MY SHOULDER!
COUNT YOURSELF LUCKY I DIDN'T AIM FOR YOUR BLACK HEART!
NOW SPILL THE BEANS! WHO'S WATERMAN?
HE . . . HE'S MANNY VASS, THE GANGSTER. HE'S HOLED UP HERE PLANNIN' A COMEBACK IN NEW YORK AFTER A GANG WAR. HE WAS BORED. THAT'S WHY HE BOUGHT THOSE JOINTS IN TOWN! HE WAS AMUSIN' HISSELF.
By the time the police arrived King Cobra had changed back into Bill King . . .
THOSE TWO MEANT TO KILL ME, OFFICER. BUT KING COBRA TURNED THE TABLES.
RIGHT, MISTER. WE'LL LOCK 'EM UP.
But later it was King Cobra who scaled the wall surrounding Vass's mansion . . .
CURRENT ON! THAT'LL FINISH KING COBRA.
PHEW! MY INSULATED GAUNTLETS SAVED ME! THERE'S ENOUGH CURRENT IN THAT WIRE TO KILL A HERD OF ELEPHANTS!
OH-OH, COMPANY!

SORRY, FELLAS! COBRA HIDE ISN'T TO BE RECOMMENDED FOR THE DENTURED.
HEY, WHAT'S UP WIV 'EM DOGS?
AND WHERE'S KING COBRA?
HE'S RIGHT HERE!
TWO LESS TO DEAL WITH! NOW TO FIND VASS!
KRAAASH
FOOLS! YOUR BULLETS ARE NO USE! MY RIFLE GRENADE WILL BLAST HIM TO PIECES!
BAAM

A NICE SOFT CATCH . . . NOT ENOUGH TO SET OFF THE IMPACT FUSE!
NOW HAVE IT BACK!
KAAAUMPH
AIEEEE
YOU'RE GOING NOWHERE, VASS!
NOW, YOU GREAT HEAP OF LARD, SIGN BACK ALL THE PROPERTY YOU FORCED THOSE POOR PEOPLE TO SELL! ALSO I WANT A CONFESSION OF EVERY CRIME YOU COMMITTED.
Later—
WELL, I'M OFF NOW, BOBBY. GOT MY STORY — AND THOSE GANGSTERS ARE ALL NICELY LOCKED UP IN JAIL. I'VE LEFT YOU A TIP IN THE GUEST-ROOM.
G . . . GEE!
Thanks for your help in beating the gangsters. King Cobra
COWARDLY NEWSHOUND. GOOD RIDDANCE!
I DON'T KNOW THOUGH! WHERE DID HE GET THE MASK? AND HOW COME KING COBRA ONLY SHOWED UP WHEN HE ARRIVED?
The End

OSSIE the OUTLAW

PRINGLE was a name feared throughout the West, for all the Pringles were notorious outlaws—all, that is, except Ossie! No matter how hard he tried Ossie was no good at being bad.

One day, at a travelling show—

SPRING

John Jackson was the timid civilian clerk at Ravell Row Police Station in the foggy heart of Victorian London. But Jackson had a secret identity — Spring-heeled Jack, dreaded enemy of all evil-doers. P.C. 13 was new on the beat when . . .

AN AMBUSH! I KNEW THIRTEEN WAS AN UNLUCKY NUMBER!

John Jackson was late for duty . . .

IT'S YOUNG GEORGE GREEN! HE'S IN TROUBLE! HANG ON, I'M COMING!

ARE YOU ALL RIGHT?

ONLY THANKS TO YOU, JOHN. PHEW, THEY MEANT BUSINESS.

PERHAPS I CAN HELP. BUT NOT AS A STAMMERING, AWKWARD CLERK . . .

HEELED JACK

BLIMEY, WOT'S GOING ON?
RUN! WE'VE ATTRACTED TOO MUCH ATTENTION!

The incident was reported to the Inspector at Rovoll Row
THE FIFTH ATTACK ON A CONSTABLE THIS MONTH. I WANT ACTION! MORE PATROLS! FIND THE CULPRITS! YOU'RE NOT MILKSOPS! BEAT THEM! I WON'T HAVE MY MEN SCARED FROM THE STREETS.

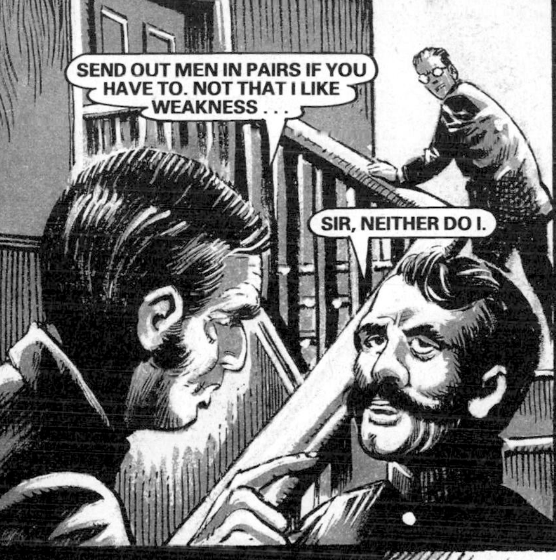
SEND OUT MEN IN PAIRS IF YOU HAVE TO. NOT THAT I LIKE WEAKNESS . . .
SIR, NEITHER DO I.

. . . IT'S TIME TO BECOME SPRING-HEELED JACK — THE LEAPING TERROR FROM THE FOG!

ALL FEAR ME, BUT THE UNDERWORLD MOST. I'LL TRY TO GUARD OUR PATROLS.

Jack kept watch and later that night . . .
AT LEAST YOU'RE NOT BY YOURSELF, YOUNG 'UN.
I'M GLAD SERGEANT DREW SENT YOU WITH ME. I HATE BEING UNLUCKY THIRTEEN.

LOOK OUT!
I'LL GET 'IM!

ONE BRUTE HAS A KNIFE! THAT'S STRANGE! HE MUST MEAN TO KILL. THIS TILE SHOULD GIVE THEM A SHOCK!

WHAT ON EARTH? THE FOG FIEND . . . HE'S ON US!

IT'S THE LEAPER! HE'S IN LEAGUE WITH THE ATTACKERS!
HE DOESN'T REALISE I SAVED HIM.

SCUM, YOU'RE MINE! I WISH TO HAVE WORDS WITH YOU!

TALK — OR I'LL DROP YOU! I NEED ANSWERS!
WE WERE PAID! SOMEONE WANTS THE POLICE ATTACKED. NO ONE'S SEEN THE BLOKE'S FACE.

HE TOLD US TO MAKE AN EXAMPLE! TO KILL P.C. 13! MAKE IT A REAL UNLUCKY NUMBER.

HE KNOWS NOTHING MORE! I MUST RETURN.
LOOK!

NOW TO RETURN TO BEING A SIMPLE CLERK!

Next day . . .
THIRTEEN, YOU SEEM TO DRAW TROUBLE! FOR HEAVEN'S SAKE PUT THE MAN SOMEWHERE SAFE, SERGEANT!
I'VE GOT HIM DOWN TO PATROL THE HIGH STREET, SIR! HE'LL KEEP OUT OF ALLEYS AND STAY IN THE LIGHT.

JACKSON, MAKE COPIES OF MY REPORT.
LATER, SERGEANT! FIRST I THINK I'D BETTER KEEP AN EYE ON YOUNG THIRTEEN!

Later . . .
HE'S SAFE ENOUGH THERE. PERHAPS I'M WASTING MY TIME.

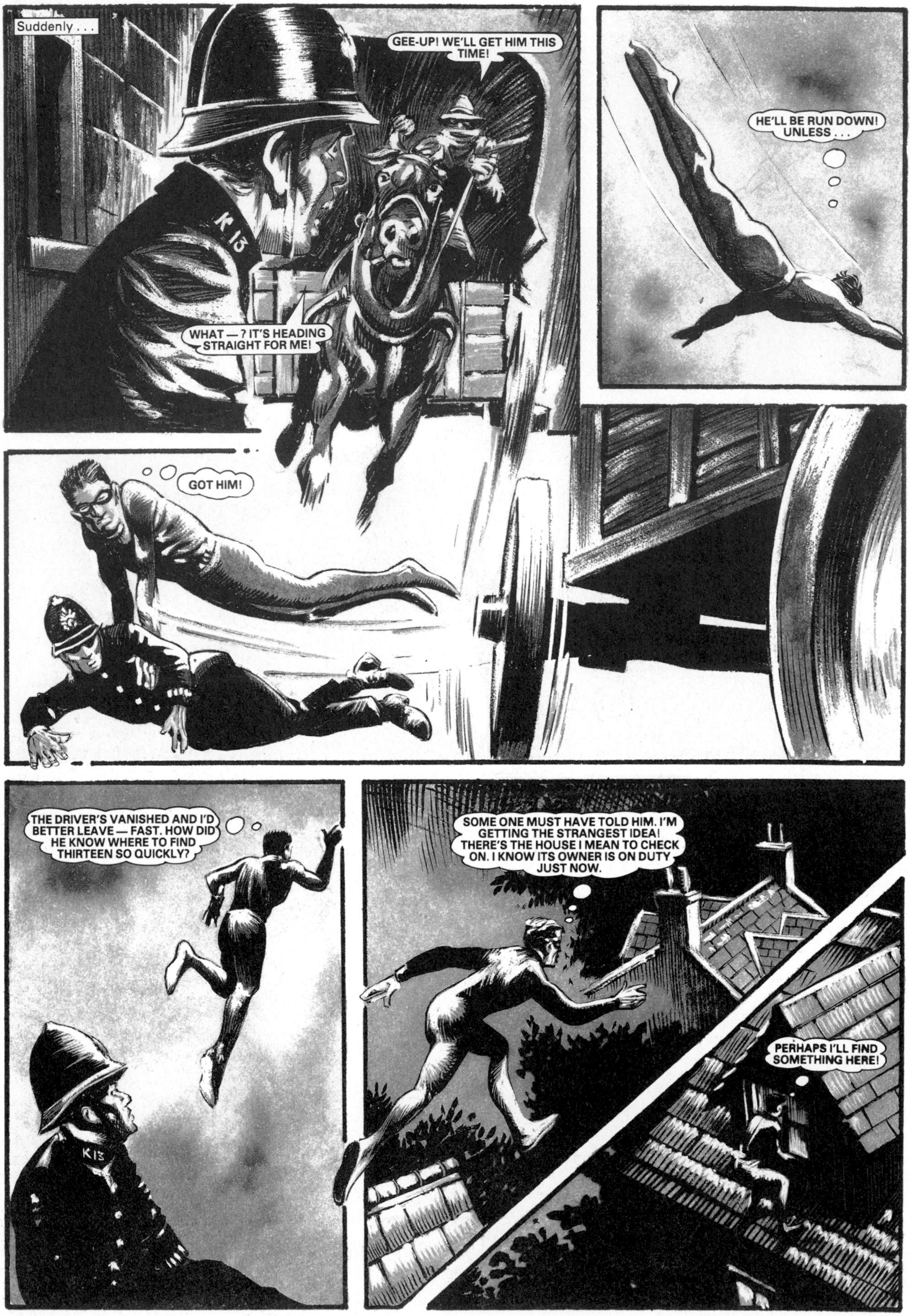

Suddenly . . .

GEE-UP! WE'LL GET HIM THIS TIME!

WHAT — ? IT'S HEADING STRAIGHT FOR ME!

HE'LL BE RUN DOWN! UNLESS . . .

GOT HIM!

THERE'S NOTHING HERE TO PROVE ANYTHING! PERHAPS I'M MISTAKEN.

But outside . . .
THERE'S A LIGHT ON IN MY STUDY! SURELY A SERVANT WOULDN'T DARE . . .

NO SIGN OF A BREAK-IN — BUT SOME ONE WAS HERE! THE LETTER! HAS SOME DEVIL FOUND IT?

From a secret drawer . . .
THANK HEAVENS, IT'S STILL HERE! IF IT FELL INTO THE WRONG HANDS . . .

I'LL TAKE THAT, INSPECTOR! IT'S MY GUESS IT'LL EXPLAIN THE ATTACKS ON YOUNG THIRTEEN!
AAAH! SPRING-HEELED JACK!

IT'S ABOUT A WILL! SO YOUNG P.C. 13 WILL BE HEIR TO A SMALL FORTUNE — UNLESS HE DIES FIRST! SHOULD THAT HAPPEN, YOU'RE NEXT IN LINE. SO YOU ARE THE ONE WHO WANTS HIM KILLED.

YOU KNEW ABOUT EVERY PATROL. YOU COULD FIND KILLERS AND TELL THEM WHERE TO FIND THIRTEEN!

YOU FIEND — I'LL . . .
NO! I'LL HAVE THIS!

NO ONE WILL BELIEVE IT. THERE'S NO PROOF I ARRANGED THE ATTACKS! YOU'RE POWERLESS.

FOOL, I CAN ALWAYS FIND YOU. IF ANYTHING HAPPENS TO P.C. 13 — BEWARE! I AM JUSTICE!

Next day . . .
TRUST AN INSPECTOR TO BE TAKEN ILL AND RESIGN! YOU'D BETTER REWRITE ALL THE REPORTS FOR HIS REPLACEMENT.
SO THE INSPECTOR IS GOING TO CLEAR OUT! PERHAPS THAT'S THE BEST THING HE COULD HAVE DONE!

Three weeks later . . .
I CAN'T BELIEVE IT. I'VE COME INTO A FORTUNE FROM A DISTANT RELATIVE. I NEVER EVEN KNEW THE OLD BOY.
K13

I'LL BE LEAVING THE FORCE, JOHN. BEING P.C. 13 TURNED OUT TO BE LUCKY AFTER ALL.
K13 K13
LUCKIER THAN YOU'LL EVER KNOW — THANKS TO SPRING-HEELED JACK!
The End

CONTINUED FROM PAGE 72.

Showdown

CHAPTER FOUR

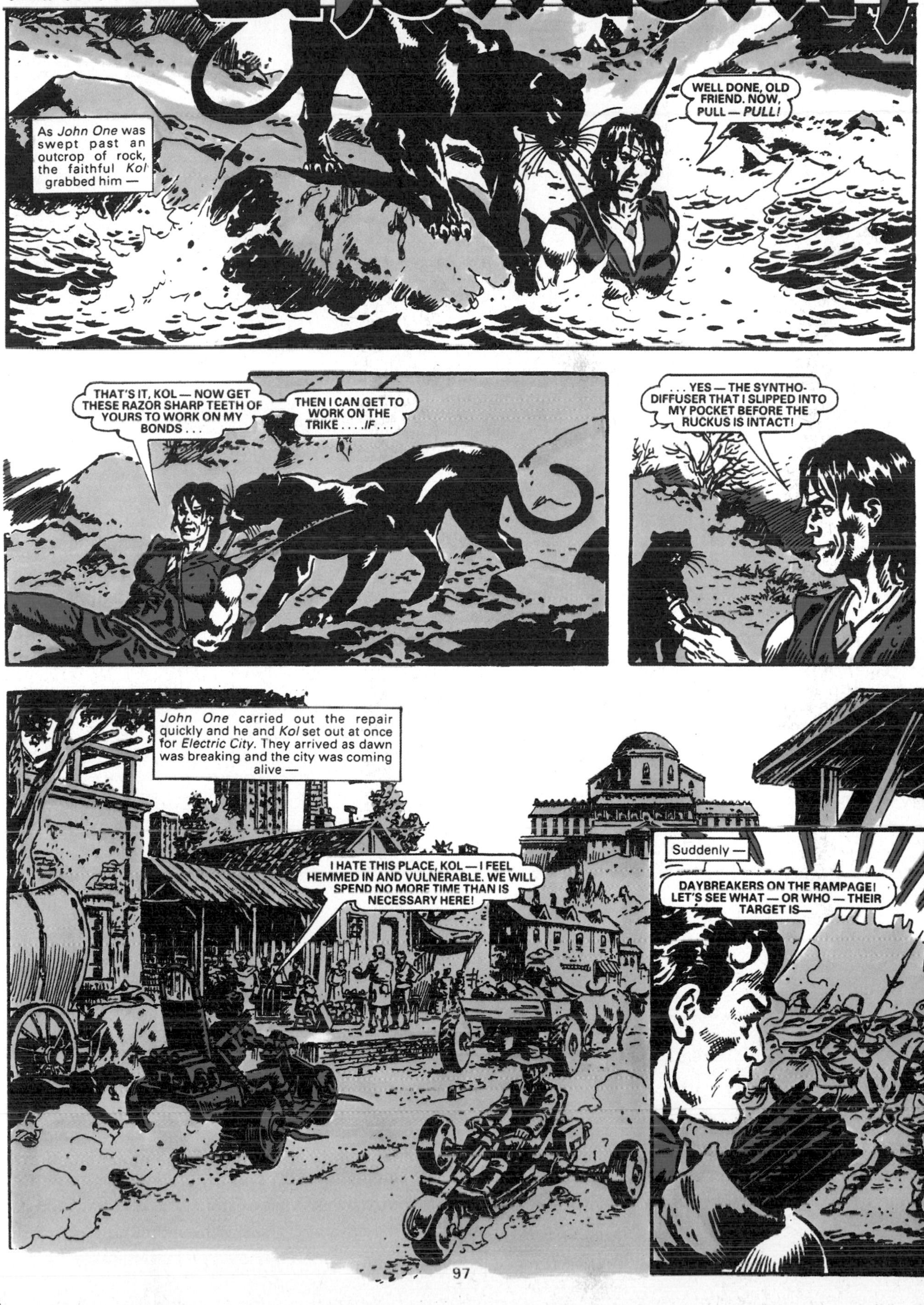

John One carried out the repair quickly and he and *Kol* set out at once for *Electric City*. They arrived as dawn was breaking and the city was coming alive —

I HATE THIS PLACE, KOL — I FEEL HEMMED IN AND VULNERABLE. WE WILL SPEND NO MORE TIME THAN IS NECESSARY HERE!

Suddenly —

DAYBREAKERS ON THE RAMPAGE! LET'S SEE WHAT — OR WHO — THEIR TARGET IS—

TAKE THE REBEL SCUM TO THE CELLS!
THEY'VE FOUND A RESISTANCE CELL. TIME WE LENT A HAND, KOL . . .
One Daybreaker fell to John One's arrow; another to Kol . . . then —
ANOTHER REBEL PIG! TAKE HIM WITH A PARA-BLAST—!
AA-AA-AAH!
A blast of searing light and the luckless pair were immobilised . . .
. . . and when John One came to, he was in Technolord Bork's dungeons —
THANKS FOR YOUR HELP, STRANGER. ALAS — IT WAS IN VAIN . . .
SO NOW YOU WILL JOIN US IN THE ARENA . . . FIGHTING TO THE DEATH FOR THE ENTERTAINMENT OF THE TECHNOS. THE FATE OF ALL CAPTURED REBELS . . .
I AM CORVEL, THE LEADER, AND THESE ARE MY LIEUTENANTS. WITHOUT US, THE RESISTANCE WILL CRUMBLE. THEN WHO WILL STOP BORK AND HIS TAME TEACHERS PRODUCING GERM GAS AT QUO-POWER EIGHT — ?
GERM GAS . . . AT QUO-POWER EIGHT?
MY FATHER IS THERE. HE WOULDN'T CO-OPERATE WITH SUCH EVIL . . .
HUSH, YOU TWO, HERE COME THE GUARDS!

For several days the rebels were put to work tarring the woodwork of the arena where the 'gladiators' would do battle. As John One plotted his escape . . . Bork was planning a nasty surprise for him.
GOT TO GET OUT OF HERE AND REACH MY FATHER. BUT HOW—?
I LIKE IT! IT IS A BRILLIANT IDEA OF MINE TO HAVE THAT BLACK PANTHER AND HIS MASTER FIGHT EACH OTHER IN THE ARENA . . .
BUT WILL THE BEAST ATTACK HIS MASTER —?
LORD BORK, THE BEAST IS STARVING. ALSO WE WILL DESTROY HIS MASTER'S SCENT BY DOUSING HIM IN TURPENTINE, AND HE WILL WEAR A MASK . . .
THE STUPID BEAST WILL NOT RECOGNISE HIM!
As the 'gladiators' were prepared for the contest, John One was baffled by the special treatment he received . . . but all became clear the instant he stepped into the arena —!
IT'S KOL — AND HE DOESN'T RECOGNISE ME. I SMELL DIFFERENT, LOOK DIFFERENT . . .
Kol stalked John One . . . it was a clear case of kill or be killed, yet John One hesitated, a plan forming in his mind . . .
. . . BUT MY VOICE IS STILL THE SAME — YES — AND I CAN USE THIS TORCH—
COME ON, KOL. GET ME — HUP! THE OLD GAME — REMEMBER —?

AND NOW HE IS EITHER READY FOR THE NEXT MOVE THAT WE USED TO PRACTISE — OR HE TEARS MY THROAT OUT . . .
HU-UP! YES — HE REMEMBERS . . .
AA-AAH!
Kol created havoc among the guards while John One rallied the rebels —
CORVEL! YOUR MEN ARE ARMED FOR THE CONTESTS —! BID THEM STRIKE — NOW!
John One hurled the flaming torch into a barrel of highly inflammable tar.
WITH LUCK THIS WILL SET ALIGHT THIS WHOLE ROTTEN ARENA . . .
YOU AND YOUR MEN HAVE THINGS UNDER CONTROL NOW, CORVEL. I'M LEAVING. WHERE CAN WE MEET LATER?
ASTRO-RIDGE — THE OLD ROCKET LAUNCH SITE. GOOD LUCK — AND THANKS!
John One had earlier found out where his power-trike had been secured.
THERE'S OUR THREE-WHEELED FRIEND, KOL. LET'S GO . . .
BY THE SOUND OF THINGS, CORVEL AND HIS MEN HAVE CLEANED UP IN THERE. WE'LL MAKE STRAIGHT FOR ASTRO-RIDGE.

On *Astro Ridge* . . .

WE ARE ON OUR WAY TO JOIN OTHER REBELS IN THE PERVAL MINE, JOHN ONE. EVERY MINUTE WASTED ENDANGERS US, BUT HOW CAN I HELP YOU—?

I HAVE TO BE SURE ABOUT THAT QUO-POWER EIGHT PLACE. MY *FATHER* IS A TEACHER WORKING THERE—

THEN YOUR FATHER IS OUR *ENEMY*, JOHN ONE. IF THE GERM GAS IS PERFECTED . . . *WE ARE ALL LOST!*

I CANNOT BELIEVE MY FATHER WOULD BE INVOLVED IN SUCH A PROJECT. SOMEHOW I MUST FIND HIM AND TALK TO HIM—!

John One headed straight for *Quo-Power Eight* —

THERE IT IS, KOL . . . AND LIGHTLY GUARDED. NO-ONE WOULD DARE SABOTAGE IT FOR FEAR OF RELEASING THE DEADLY GERM GAS . . .

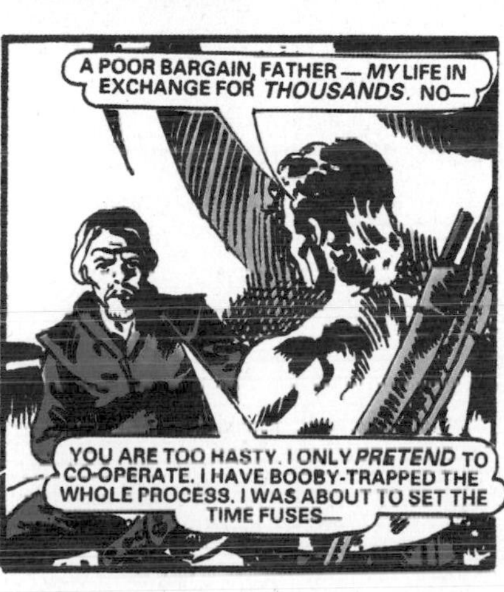

— THE HEAT OF THE EXPLOSIONS WILL KILL THE GERMS.
FATHER, I MISJUDGED YOU. NOW DO ME A FAVOUR — SET YOUR TIME FUSES FOR NOON, TWO DAYS FROM TODAY . . .
John One explained his plan to his father, then left. But some time later, outside Quo-Power Eight —
THE PERIMETER GUARDS HAVE BEEN ATTACKED. GET THEM TO THE SICK BAY . . . AND MAKE THEM TALK —!
Remembering Corvel's words, John One headed for the old Perval mine-workings where he and his men were hiding with other rebels —
AND IF YOUR FATHER IS RIGHT AND HE DOES BLOW UP QUO-POWER EIGHT . . . HOW DOES THIS HELP US GET RID OF BORK?
BORK AND HIS LIEUTENANTS WILL THINK THE GERMS ARE LOOSE! THEY'LL PANIC . . . HEAD FOR THE HILLS . . . AND THERE IS ONLY ONE ROUTE TO THE HILLS—
MMM . . . PLENTY GOOD AMBUSH SPOTS ON IT. IF WE PULL IT OFF, WE GET BORK AND HIS ADVISORS . . .
THE KINGDOM WILL BE TEMPORARILY LEADERLESS AND RIPE FOR TAKE-OVER . . . BY JUST MEN—!
On the morning of the day in question, Mathor laid his explosive charges. But at that moment in the sickbay, one of the wounded guards came to . . . briefly — but it was enough —!
THE TIMER IS SET FOR NOON EXACTLY. THE CHARGE WILL TAKE THIS WHOLE PLACE APART . . .
ATTACKED . . . MAN AND . . . AND BLACK CAT . . . AA . . .
MAN AND —? JOHN ONE! THE TEACHER MATHOR'S SON . . . SABOTAGE . . .
Mathor was beaten mercilessly, but he would not talk.
THERE IS ONE WAY TO MAKE THE FOOL TALK. IF HE HAS SABOTAGED THE PLANT, HE COULD ONLY HAVE DONE SO IN THE PLACE WHERE HE WORKS . . . SO . . .

Mathor was returned to his workplace —
LEAVE HIM ALONE HERE . . . TO SWEAT! HE WILL BE THE FIRST VICTIM OF ANY SABOTAGE HE HAS PLANNED — UNLESS HE CHANGES HIS MIND AND NEUTRALISES IT!
NEVER! BUT THE BOMB IS DUE TO EXPLODE IN ONE HOUR . . .
Later, on a slope overlooking the road from Electric City —
TWO MINUTES TO NOON. ARE YOUR MEN IN POSITION, CORVEL?
YES, JOHN ONE. THE AMBUSH IS LAID.
At exactly noon . . . Mathor's charges went off — and had the desired effect on Technolord Bork!
EXPLOSION AT QUO-POWER EIGHT, MY LORD—
WHAT—? THE — THE GERMS WILL BE RELEASED. CALL MY ADVISORS — WE MUST TAKE TO THE HILLS AT ONCE!
Electric City was in a panic, the exits blocked by fleeing citizens — but Bork's escort ruthlessly carved a way through —
MAKE WAY FOR YOUR LORD AND MASTER, COWARDLY SCUM —!
Bork's fleeing column charged blindly into Corvel's ambush.
CRUMP!
THE ROAD IS BLOCKED AHEAD — AND NOW BEHIND TOO. WE ARE TRAPPED!
THEY'RE ONLY A RABBLE OF ILL-ARMED REBELS. STAND AND FIGHT, FOOLS—!

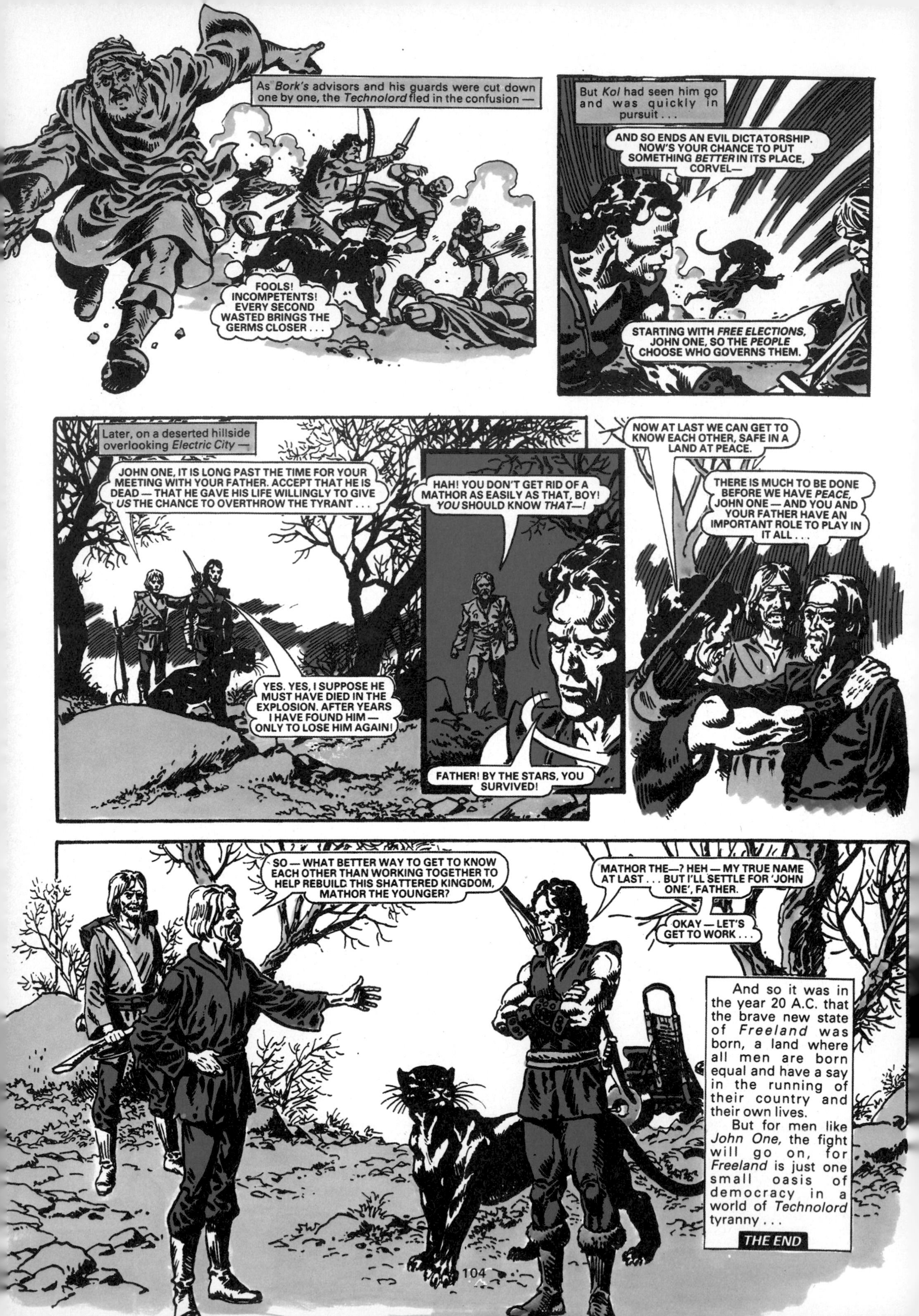

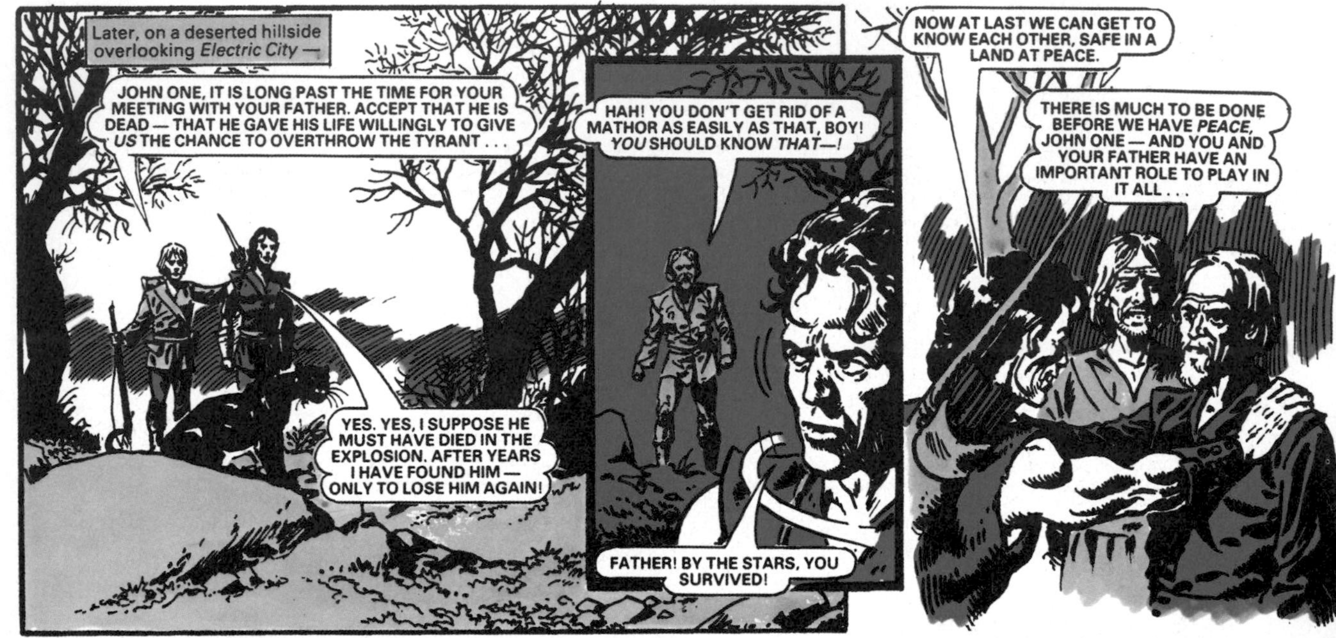

SO — WHAT BETTER WAY TO GET TO KNOW EACH OTHER THAN WORKING TOGETHER TO HELP REBUILD THIS SHATTERED KINGDOM, MATHOR THE YOUNGER?

MATHOR THE—? HEH — MY TRUE NAME AT LAST . . . BUT I'LL SETTLE FOR 'JOHN ONE', FATHER.

OKAY — LET'S GET TO WORK . . .

And so it was in the year 20 A.C. that the brave new state of *Freeland* was born, a land where all men are born equal and have a say in the running of their country and their own lives.

But for men like *John One,* the fight will go on, for *Freeland* is just one small oasis of democracy in a world of *Technolord* tyranny . . .

THE END

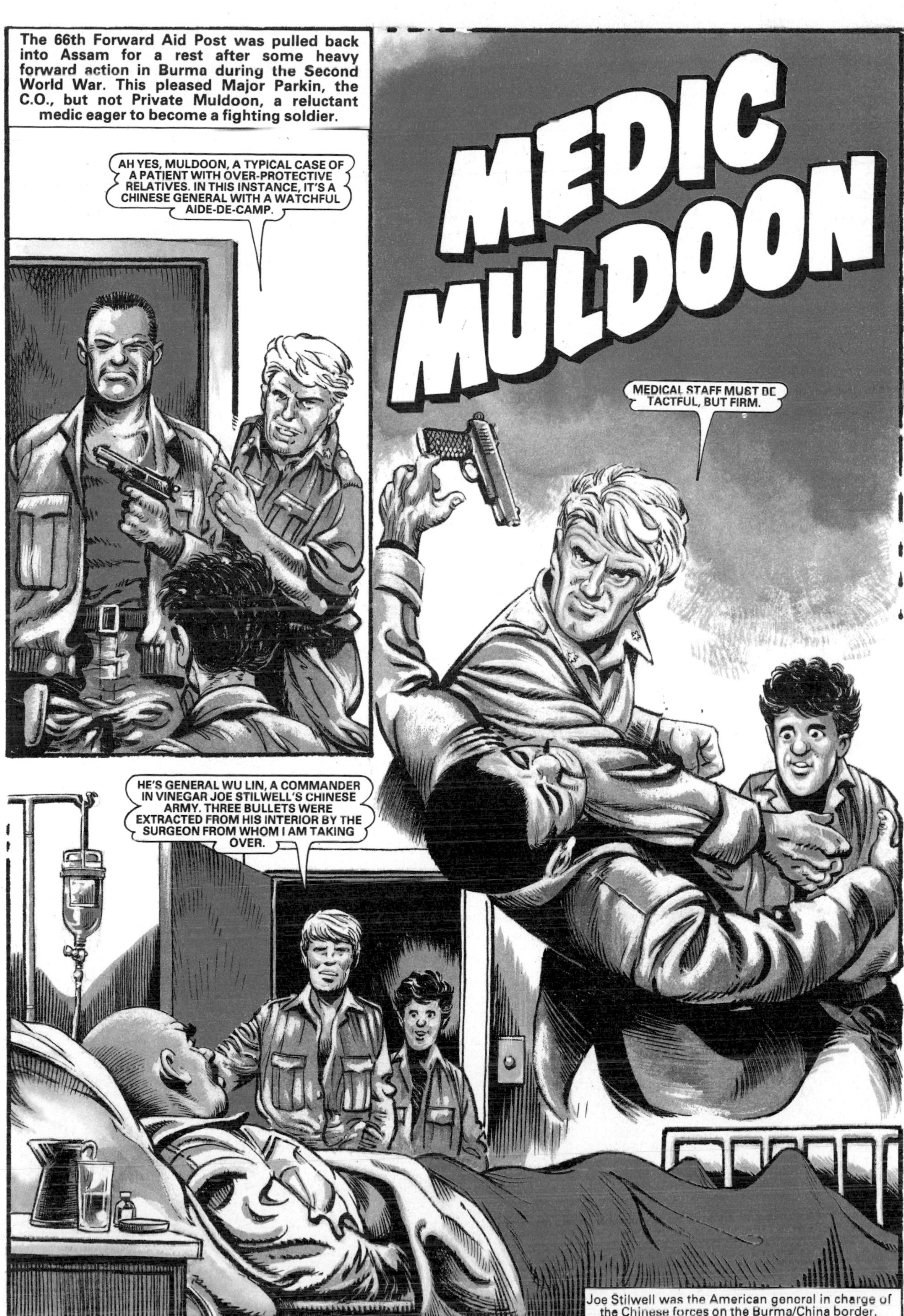
The 66th Forward Aid Post was pulled back into Assam for a rest after some heavy forward action in Burma during the Second World War. This pleased Major Parkin, the C.O., but not Private Muldoon, a reluctant medic eager to become a fighting soldier.
MEDIC MULDOON
AH YES, MULDOON, A TYPICAL CASE OF A PATIENT WITH OVER-PROTECTIVE RELATIVES. IN THIS INSTANCE, IT'S A CHINESE GENERAL WITH A WATCHFUL AIDE-DE-CAMP.
MEDICAL STAFF MUST BE TACTFUL, BUT FIRM.
HE'S GENERAL WU LIN, A COMMANDER IN VINEGAR JOE STILWELL'S CHINESE ARMY. THREE BULLETS WERE EXTRACTED FROM HIS INTERIOR BY THE SURGEON FROM WHOM I AM TAKING OVER.
Joe Stilwell was the American general in charge of the Chinese forces on the Burma/China border.

Muldoon was detailed . . .

YOU FLY TO LEDO AND YOU FLY STRAIGHT BACK. NO NEED TO EVEN GET OUT OF THE PLANE, MULDOON!

YESSIR! I'LL DO MY BEST NOT TO GET LOST.

A JAP ZERO! DIVE! DIVE!

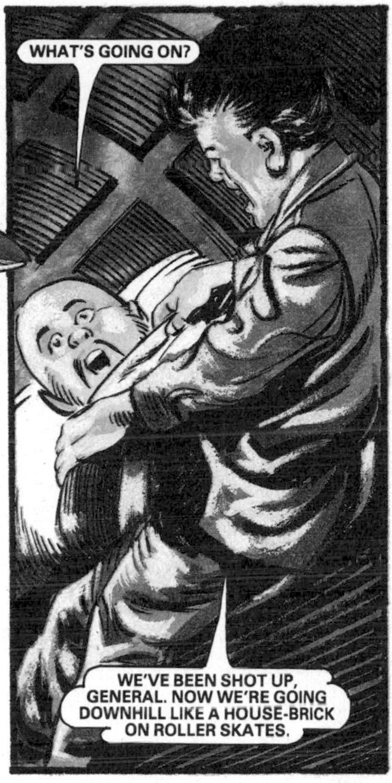
WHAT'S GOING ON?
WE'VE BEEN SHOT UP, GENERAL. NOW WE'RE GOING DOWNHILL LIKE A HOUSE-BRICK ON ROLLER SKATES.

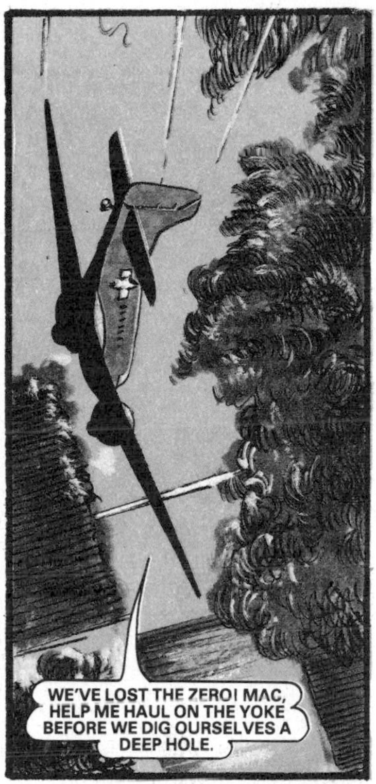
WE'VE LOST THE ZERO! MAC, HELP ME HAUL ON THE YOKE BEFORE WE DIG OURSELVES A DEEP HOLE.

WE'RE COMING OUT. ZOWIE! THAT WAS CLOSE.
NO SIGN OF THE ZERO. MUST HAVE BEEN A PROWLER ON LONG-RANGE TANKS. HE WOULDN'T HAVE THE FUEL TO FOLLOW US DOWN!

SORRY, GENERAL. YOUR AIDE'S DEAD.
I'M SORRY TOO. HE WAS A GOOD AND DUTIFUL SON.

GENTS, WE GOT A MITE OF TROUBLE. OIL PRESSURE'S DOWN AND THE SKIPPER AIMS TO TRY FOR A LANDING ON SOME PADDY-FIELDS. THERE'S A VILLAGE NEARBY!

SKIPPER, WE'D BE SAFER PANCAKING.
SURE, MAC, BUT WE'LL NEVER TAKE OFF AGAIN IF WE LAND WITH THE WHEELS UP.

Muldoon found he had company . . .

THERE'S THE MACHINE-GUN THAT FIRED ON US. A WOODPECKER UP IN THAT WATCH-TOWER.
THAT GUN IS WHAT WE NEED FOR FIRE-POWER.
BUB, YOU SURE ARE AN UNUSUAL KIND OF PILL-PUSHER.
JUST AS WELL MAJOR PARKIN CAN'T SEE ME NOW. STILL, HERE WE GO!
YOU'VE SPOTTED ME BUT TOO LATE, MY YELLOW FRIENDS!

THIS WON'T TAKE LONG! THEY'VE NO IDEA!

YES, SIR. ONE UNUSUAL PILL-PUSHER!

I'LL BE WITH YOU SOON AS I GET THIS WOODPECKER OFF ITS TRIPOD.
BUB, I DON'T RECKON YOU'RE GOING TO HAVE TIME FOR THAT. LOOK WHAT'S COMING OUR WAY.

THAT JAP PATROL HAS CHANGED ITS MIND ABOUT LOOKING AT THE PLANE!

HEY, GENERAL, WHERE YOU GOING? COME BACK, YOU CRAZY COOT.

TAKE THAT, YOU NIPPONESE DOGS!

AH, IF ONLY MY STRENGTH HAD LASTED A LITTLE LONGER. SO STRIKE, DOG! DO YOUR WORST!

AARGH!

GANG UP ON MY PATIENT, WOULD YOU?

BUB, THERE'S A PLACE FOR YOU IN MY OUTFIT ANYTIME YOU WANT IT.
I WANT IT, GENERAL! YOU CAN SEND MAJOR PARKIN AN OFFICIAL ORDER SAYING I'M A FIGHTING SOLDIER AT LAST.

WE GOT IT FIXED, MEDIC. NOW ALL WE GOT TO DO IS UNSTICK THE OLD BUS OFF THIS PADDY.
JUST LET ME GET THE GENERAL ON BOARD!

The Dakota lumbered into the air . . .
COME ON NOW, GENERAL! DON'T DIE ON ME NOW.

An hour later . . .
WHAT HAPPENED? URH — I MUST HAVE PASSED OUT.
YOUR WOUND HAD OPENED UP AND YOU WENT INTO SHOCK. I HAD TO DO SOME QUICK DOCTORING AND TRANSFUSE YOU WITH A PINT OF MY OWN GOOD QUALITY TYPE-O BLOOD.

MULDOON, YOU ARE ONE HECK OF A SOLDIER, BUT I'M TAKING BACK MY OFFER. THAT STUCK-UP MAJOR IS RIGHT ABOUT YOU BEING TOO GOOD A MEDIC TO BE WASTED ANYWHERE ELSE.
HUH!

Muldoon safely delivered the general then was flown back to an angry Major Parkin . . .
SO NOW THE CHINESE ARE GIVING YOU A DECORATION, EH? MULDOON, YOU KNOW HOW I FEEL ABOUT YOU MIXING IN VIOLENT AND UNMEDICAL MATTERS.
I KNOW, SIR. I SUPPOSE IT'LL BE BEHIND THE COOKHOUSE AS USUAL, SIR.

Major Parkin delivered one of his lectures . . .

MULDOON, I REALLY DO REGRET THE NEED FOR THESE DISCUSSIONS WITH YOU.
I'M SURE YOU DON'T REGRET THEM AS MUCH AS I DO, SIR.
THE END

THE T AINING OF A RED DEVIL

When it was decided in 1940 to form an airborne corps for the British Army, there was no provision for the training of such a force. However, a centre was soon established at Ringwood, near Manchester, and it was here that Britian's paratroops were trained for the rest of the Second World War.

Put through a rigorous physical training course, the potential paras had then to learn to jump safely. Many strange devices were used, including dummy fuselages, high towers and barrage balloons. Finally, the novice paratrooper made his jumps from an aircraft, initially these were converted Whitley bombers. After his training was complete and he had done the requisite number of jumps, the para was awarded his coveted wings. He was now a member of that elite force the "Red Devils".

All kitted up, trainee paras sit in the dummy fuselage of an aircraft waiting to make a drop.

A parachute was attached to the crane-like structure at the top of the tower. The novice jumper dropped to the ground but his speed was controlled so that he could be taught to land properly.

The basket slung below this barrage balloon was the place from which most paras did this first "free" jump. An instructor on the ground could still give advice.

A para makes his jump from a Whitley. The static line which opened the parachute of the previous jumper can be seen streaming out.

THE LEGEND
Three games to the end of the season and Norrington City . . . known as the Reds 'n' the Blues . . . were one of five teams still in with a chance of the Championship title. City were playing well and no one in the side was showing better form than mid-field power-house, Rab McLaren. A big money signing at the start of the season, McLaren was the idol of the City fans but to his team-mates . . . he was a pain!
MAKE WAY, LADS! GIMME ROOM. THE LEGEND HAS A PHOTO SESSION!
BIG-HEAD'S HERE!
HE'S ALL MOUTH!
A STORY OF THE FAMOUS REDS 'N' BLUES!
NICE ONE, RAB! HOLD IT LIKE THAT!
YOU CAN'T KICK WITH YOUR LEFT FOOT, McLAREN!
I'VE SCORED MORE GOALS WITH MY LEFT THAN YOU'VE COLLECTED WITH BOTH FEET, TORRIE! MIND YOU . . . THAT'S NOT DIFFICULT.
ANY ONE OF FIVE TEAMS CAN WIN THE CHAMPIONSHIP, RAB! HOW DO YOU RATE CITY'S CHANCE?
YOU'RE JOKING AREN'T YOU? WITH ME IN THE TEAM . . . CITY CAN'T LOSE, MATE!
Mitre 25

H

PLAYERS ONLY
RAB! YOU COULD BE VOTED FOOTBALLER OF THE YEAR! HOW DO YOU RATE YOURSELF FOR THAT?
NO CONTEST IS IT? IT'S GOT TO BE ME! I'M THE BEST — THE LEGEND! GOTTA GO . . . SEE YOU LATER! KEEP SMILING!

The rest of the team were getting ready for the home game against Chelford—
COME ON! I'M READY! THE FANS WANT TO WATCH ME KICKING IN! EXTRA TREAT FOR 'EM, AIN'T IT! SEE THE GREAT MAN!
YEAH . . RIGHT ENOUGH, McLAREN. AFTER ALL — WE'RE ONLY HERE TO MAKE UP THE NUMBERS!
Rab McLaren knew how to put on a show—
FIFTEEN . . . SIXTEEN . . . SEVENTEEN . . .
YEAAHHHHH! MAKE IT FIFTY, RABBIE!

YEAAAAHHHHH!! GREAT SAVE!
HECK . . . I MUST HAVE MISHIT IT! CLEM DOESN'T USUALLY GET NEAR MY SHOTS!

HA! MADE YOU WORK FOR THAT ONE EH, CLEM? HOW DOES IT FEEL TO EVENTUALLY SAVE A LEGEND PILEDRIVER?
CAN'T YOU GIVE YOUR MOUTH A REST, McLAREN? YOUR TEETH MUST BE GETTING PRETTY FED UP OF ALWAYS SEEING DAYLIGHT!

Early in the game—
YEAAHHH! GREAT TACKLE, RABBIE!
YOURS, FRASER! DO SOMETHING WITH IT!

He was always available—
DON'T PASS IT BACK TO CLEM, THEY'VE GOT HIM COVERED. GIMME IT OUT HERE!

Rab burst forward . . . then released striker Joe Johnson—
USE IT, SON . . . I'VE DONE ALL THE HARD WORK!

Joe didn't miss chances like that—
IT'S THERE! GREAT STRIKE!

Near the end—
OHHHHHHH! UNLUCKY, DANNY!
YEAH . . . BUT LOOK WHO'S COMING TO MEET IT!

ALWAYS GOES OVER TO THAT MILKO ADVERTISEMENT, DOESN'T HE?
THEY PAY HIM TO DO IT! CHEAP PUBLICITY FOR 'EM!

City won the game 2-0. On the Monday morning at the training ground . . .
I HOPE YOU'RE GOING TO PUT YOUR MILKO MONEY IN THE PLAYERS' POOL, RAB? WE KNOW YOU'RE TIED IN WITH THEM!
IN THE PLAYERS' POOL? YOU'RE JOKING, TORRIE. WHAT I EARN OUTSIDE THE GAME . . . I KEEP! SIMPLE AS THAT!

FOOTBALL'S A TEAM GAME, YOU CREEP!
YEAH! WE ALL PULL TOGETHER . . . AND SHARE THE PERKS!
ONLY I PULL HARDER THAN MOST, DON'T I? WHY DO YOU THINK THEY CALL ME THE LEGEND, EH?

THEY CALL YOU THE LEGEND . . . BECAUSE YOU FLAMING WELL INVENTED THE NAME YOURSELF! BUT YOU AIN'T A LEGEND TO US, MATE . . . YOU'RE JUST A PAIN! A BIG, SELFISH PAIN!

YOU'RE SMALL PEOPLE! THE CROWDS DON'T TURN UP TO WATCH YOU. IT'S ME THEY WANT TO SEE . . . AND DON'T YOU FORGET IT!
I'LL PLANT ONE ON HIM . . . I SWEAR I'LL PLANT ONE ON HIM!
COOL IT, SAM! DON'T LET HIM WIND YOU UP!

I'VE HAD IT UP TO HERE WITH McLAREN! IF THE BOSS INCLUDES HIM IN SATURDAY'S TEAM . . . THEN HE CAN COUNT ME OUT! I WON'T PLAY.
ME, TOO! HE'S NOT A TEAM MAN . . . HE PLAYS FOR HIMSELF!
EVERYTHING HE DOES . . . IS FOR HIMSELF!

Later, in the players' leisure room, Sam Torrie handed a petition to skipper Garry Fraser—
WE'VE ALL SIGNED, GARRY! EVERY FIRST TEAM SQUAD NAME IS ON THAT PAPER. IF McLAREN PLAYS . . . WE DON'T! WE GO ON STRIKE!
I KNOW WHAT YOU MEAN. I'LL TAKE IT TO THE BOSS! BUT I CAN'T SEE IT DOING MUCH GOOD THOUGH!

Manager Ken Robbins received the petition—
THEY DON'T LIKE McLAREN, DINGER! BUT I CAN'T LET THE PLAYERS DECIDE TEAM SELECTION!
VENUE
McLAREN'S GOOD! BUT HE GETS PEOPLE'S BACKS UP. THE FUNNY THING IS — I DON'T THINK HE REALISES WHAT HE'S DOING!

THERE'S NO WAY I'M DROPPING McLAREN . . . TO PLEASE ANYONE! THE REST OF THE PLAYERS HAVE GOT TO REALISE THAT WHATEVER ELSE McLAREN IS — HE'S A GOOD PLAYER! HE WORKS HARD FOR THE TEAM.
VENUE
HE'S A BIG-HEAD AND A LOUD-MOUTH, TOO! BUT . . . I AGREE. HE'S TOO VALUABLE TO LEAVE OUT!

So, when Ken Robbins posted the team-list for the Oldcastle game—
McLAREN'S IN!
AND HE STAYS IN, SAM! I KNOW HOW YOU ALL FEEL ABOUT HIM . . . BUT HE'S WORTH HIS PLACE. PUT UP WITH HIM UNTIL WE'VE WON OR LOST THE CHAMPIONSHIP. THEN WE'LL SEE . . .

YEAH? WHAT WILL WE SEE?
THAT'S UP TO ME TO DECIDE, SAM. YOUR DUTY . . . AND EVERYONE'S DUTY . . . IS TO GIVE 100% NO MATTER WHO YOU PLAY ALONGSIDE!

Oldcastle defended bravely — until Joe Johnson dived bravely to connect with a Danny Keen cross—

Then just before the final whistle—
2-0! MA-GIC, DANNY!
CITY HAVE DONE IT NOW! THAT'S ANOTHER THREE VALUABLE POINTS!

It all came down to the last match of the season—
YOU KNOW THE STORY, LADS. WE WIN TODAY . . . WE'RE CHAMPIONS! WE DRAW . . . OR LOSE — EVERDON WILL TAKE THE TITLE!
WANT A PIECE OF GOOD NEWS BEFORE WE START, LADS?
YEAH? YOU MEAN YOU AIN'T PLAYING TODAY, McLAREN?

THOSE OF YOU WHO CAN READ . . . GET A LOAD OF THAT! THE PRESS BOYS GOT IT RIGHT THIS YEAR!
RAB McLAREN
FOOTBALLER OF YEAR!
CITY'S HUMAN DYNAMO GETS AWARD

FOOTBALLER OF THE YEAR? TWIT OF THE YEAR, MORE LIKE IT!
JEALOUSY WILL GET YOU NOWHERE, SUNSHINE! IT COULD HAVE HAPPENED TO ANYONE OF YOU . . . BUT YOU'RE NOT GOOD ENOUGH! SIMPLE, AIN'T IT!
THAT'S ENOUGH! WE'VE GOT A GAME — *AND* A CHAMPIONSHIP TO WIN!

YOU KNOW WHAT TO DO, LADS IF YOU WANT TO WIN. JUST GIVE ME THE BALL AND I'LL DO THE REST!
SEE OLD MOTOR MOUTH'S AT IT AGAIN!

But disaster struck in the first minute—
HECK! ONE DOWN ALREADY!
YEAH — EVERDON WILL TAKE SOME STOPPING NOW!

And on the stroke of half-time—
VENUE

YOU'RE GIVING IT AWAY! I'LL GO OUT THERE AND WIN THE GAME MYSELF! I'M NOT LOSING TO THIS BUNCH OF NO-USERS!
OKAY, McLAREN, *I'LL* DO THE PEP-TALK. YOU SIT AND LISTEN!

YOU'RE TWO DOWN . . . BUT YOU'VE GOT FORTY-FIVE MINUTES LEFT TO CHANGE THAT! YOU WANT TO BE CHAMPIONS? THEN GO OUT THERE AND DO SOMETHING ABOUT IT! IT'S ALL OR NOTHING!

Rab McLaren led the charge in the second half—

C'MON! C'MON! GET MOVING, YOU LOT! I SEEM TO BE THE ONLY ONE WORKING AROUND HERE!

A good, low cross into the box—

GET ON THE END OF THAT, KEEN!

Danny Keen made no mistake—

IT'S THERE — THAT'S US RIGHT BACK IN THE GAME!

Five minutes from the end—

TWO-ALL! McLAREN'S PUT IT IN!

Rab McLaren made the headlines again on Sunday morning—
Sunday Echo
CITY'S STAR GOES TO SPAIN!
Footballer of the Year Rab McLaren signs for Sadrid F.C. £3,000,000 Transfer Deal!
And when he turned up at the ground—
WELL, LADS . . . THE LEGEND DOES IT AGAIN! THREE MILL, EH? AND WORTH EVERY PESETA IF I SAY SO MYSELF. JUST THOUGHT I'D LOOK IN TO SAY GOODBYE!
The players all went down to the car-park—
LIKE THE WHEELS LADS? STAR PLAYERS HAVE STAR CARS! YOU GUYS WORK A BIT HARDER AND YOU MIGHT BE ABLE TO AFFORD ONE, TOO! THE CHAUFFEUR IS EXTRA!
RAB-000
GOOD LUCK NEXT SEASON! BUT IF YOU COULDN'T WIN THE LEAGUE WITH ME IN THE TEAM . . . LET'S FACE IT—YOU'VE GOT NO CHANCE WITHOUT ME!
FUNNY THAT, SIR! I'D HAVE THOUGHT YOUR TEAM-MATES WOULD HAVE GIVEN YOU A FAREWELL CHEER!
I EXPECT THEY'RE A BIT CHOKED! Y'KNOW NEAR TO TEARS TO SEE THEIR OLD PAL GO AWAY SO SUDDEN!
The farewell cheer was reserved for INSIDE the club—
YEE-HOO! HE'S FLAMING GONE!
MA-GIC! WE DON'T HAVE TO LISTEN TO LOUD-MOUTH ANY MORE!
WELL . . . WHAT DO YOU THINK, BOSS?
DINGER . . . WE'VE GOT A HAPPY TEAM AGAIN! JUST WATCH US GO NEXT SEASON!
THE END

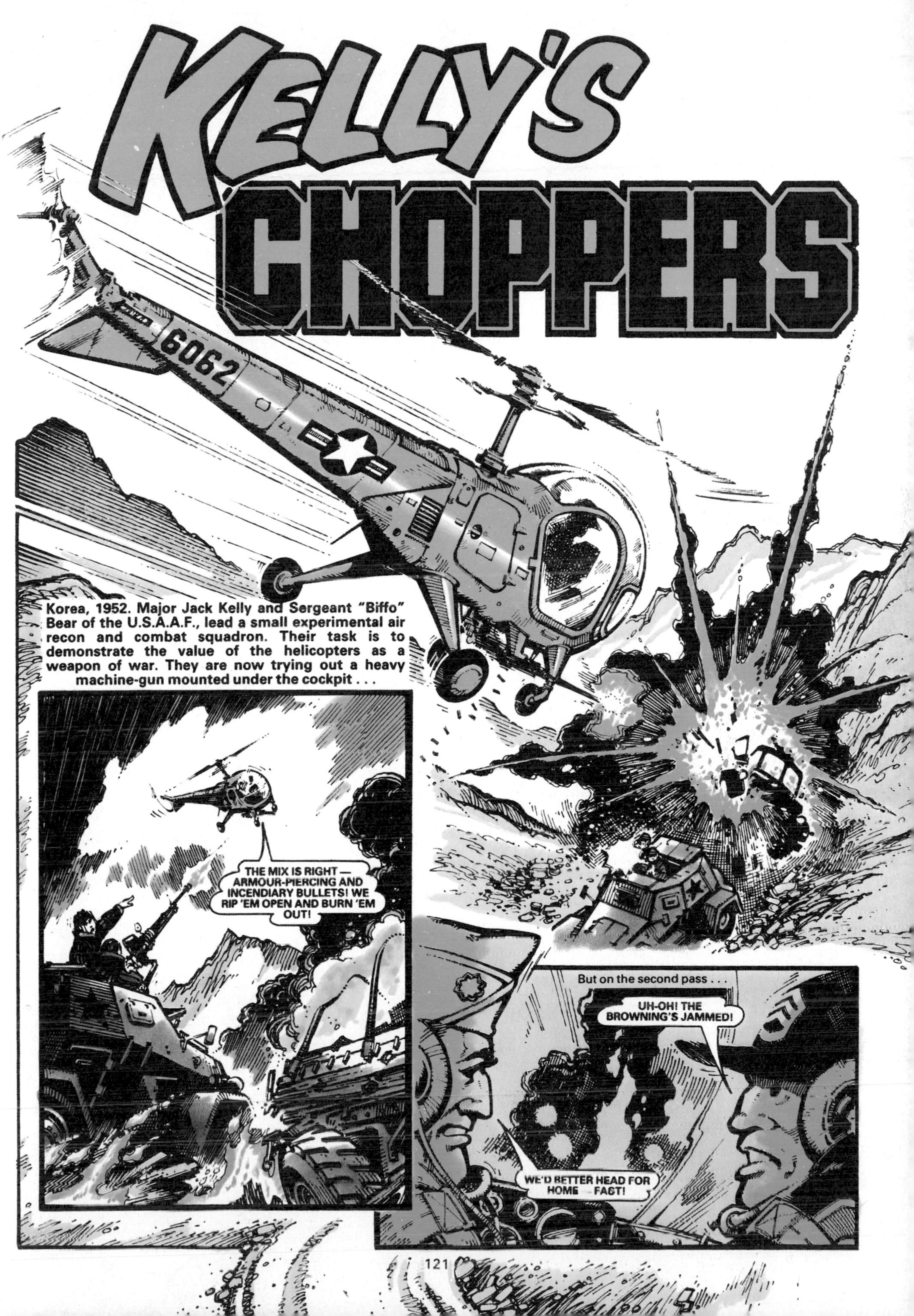

KELLY'S CHOPPERS

Korea, 1952. Major Jack Kelly and Sergeant "Biffo" Bear of the U.S.A.A.F., lead a small experimental air recon and combat squadron. Their task is to demonstrate the value of the helicopters as a weapon of war. They are now trying out a heavy machine-gun mounted under the cockpit . . .

But on the second pass . . .

When Kelly returned to base . . .
THE GOLDARN MECHANISM GOT STUCK! WHAT WE NEED ROUND HERE IS A GUY WHO UNDERSTANDS ABOUT MACHINES.
I THINK WE'VE FOUND JUST THE MAN, MAJOR. MEET LIEUTENANT "GIZMO" BENSON. HE KNOWS ALL THERE IS TO KNOW ABOUT HELICOPTERS — AND THEN SOME MORE. GENERAL PETERSON SAID WE'RE LUCKY TO HAVE HIM.
SO WHY DID THEY REALLY TRANSFER YOU HERE?
BECAUSE THEY THINK I'M CRAZY! I KEPT COMING UP WITH THESE GREAT IDEAS — AND THE BRASS KEPT TURNING THEM DOWN. IT WAS VERY FRUSTRATING.
LET'S SEE HOW YOU SHAPE UP. I'M GOING TO GIVE YOU A FREE HAND TO RUN OUR WEAPONS AND TECHNICAL DEPARTMENT.
OFFICERS MES
That night at a rear supply dump....
GOOKS! SOUND THE . . . AAAAARRRRGGGGGHHHHH!
WHERE ARE THEY?
ALL ROUND US! THOSE CREEPS CAME OUT OF THIN AIR! URRRGGGHHH!
Next morning Kelly and his men were called in.
ALMOST THE ENTIRE CAMP WIPED OUT! WE DIDN'T STAND A CHANCE, MAJOR. THE GOOKS HEADED FOR THOSE HILLS ABOUT THREE HOURS AGO.
MAYBE WE CAN STILL CATCH THEM BEFORE THEY REACH THEIR LINES. THAT'S WHY I BROUGHT MY RANGER TEAM WITH ME.
OUR KOREAN SCOUT'S PICKED UP SOME TRACKS, MAJOR! IT LOOKS LIKE THEY DRAGGED SOME WOUNDED BACK WITH THEM.
OKAY, YOU CHECK IT OUT. I'LL COVER YOU FROM UP HERE.
UGH!
AAAARRRRGGGGHHHH!
TAKE COVER!

THE BROWNING WORKS JUST FINE NOW! GIZMO MADE A FINE JOB OF SORTING OUT THE BELT FEEDING PROBLEM!
THOSE SNIPERS HELD US UP LONG ENOUGH FOR THE OTHERS TO SLIP AWAY. THEY COULD BE ANYWHERE BY NOW. WE CAN'T PICK UP THEIR TRACKS AGAIN!
OKAY, LIEUTENANT, GET YOUR BOYS BACK ON THE CHOPPER. WE'RE GOING HOME.
WE'RE UP AGAINST A GROUP OF GOOKS WHO ATTACK ONLY AT NIGHT AND ARE EXPERTS IN THE ART OF CAMOUFLAGE. OVER TO YOU, GIZMO.
THANK YOU, SIR. NOW I THINK I'VE COME UP WITH AN IDEA THAT MIGHT DO THE TRICK. I'VE FIXED THE BIG HELICOPTER TO FIRE FLARES IN A SET PATTERN TO ILLUMINATE AN ENTIRE AREA. ALL WE HAVE TO DO NOW IS WAIT FOR ANOTHER ATTACK TO TRY IT OUT!
A couple of nights later . . .
REPORT OF AN ATTACK IN SECTOR ABLE-BAKER! THIS COULD BE IT, BIFFO.
IT SHOULD TAKE US ABOUT TWENTY MINUTES TO GET THERE.
88
THE GOOKS WERE SEEN HEADED SOUTH! THEY CAN'T BE FAR AWAY!
RIGHT, WE'LL CALCULATE WHERE THEY SHOULD BE AND THEN SWITCH ON THE BIG LIGHTS!
THAT'S THE FLARE'S GONE! SEE ANYTHING YET?
NOPE! MAYBE THE MAJOR GOT IT WRONG AND THEY AIN'T IN THIS AREA. PUT HER DOWN ANYWAY!

URRRGGGHHH!
LET'S GET OUTTA HERE!
HOLY COW! THEY AMBUSHED US!
THE FLARES ARE OUT AND WE ALMOST LOST A CHOPPER!
YEAH, WE'RE NOT GOING TO FIND THEM NOW. GIZMO WILL HAVE TO COME UP WITH A BETTER IDEA.
Next morning—
YOU GOTTA BE KIDDING!
I'M SERIOUS, SIR. I GUARANTEE IT'LL WORK! IF IT DOESN'T, I'LL GO ON KITCHEN FATIGUES FOR THE REST OF THE WAR.
Later—
SPECIAL DELIVERY, SIR. THE STORES PEOPLE HAVE SCOURED THE WHOLE OF KOREA TO FIND THIS!
TAKE IT TO THE MAIN HANGER AND REPORT TO LIEUTENANT BENSON. HE'S EXPECTING YOU.
Next day—
YOU'VE TURNED US INTO A CROP-DUSTING OPERATION!
YES, SERGEANT. ONLY, THE CROPS YOU'LL BE GOING AFTER WILL BE HUMAN ONES — AND THE TYPE OF DUSTING I HAVE IN MIND WILL STUNT THEIR GROWTH!
That night an ammo dump was attacked. Kelly and his men were quickly on the scene.
I'VE PLOTTED THEIR LAST REPORTED POSITION AND THEY SHOULD BE IN THIS AREA RIGHT NOW!
OKAY, BIFFO! TURN ON THE TAPS AND LET'S GET THIS SHOW ON THE ROAD!

BLUE LEADER TO BIG MACK. WE SPRAYED THE AREA. NOW, GET DOWN THERE, RANGERS! YOU OUGHT TO SEE THEM PRETTY SOON.
ROGER! WE'RE GOIN' IN!
THERE THEY ARE!
HOLY COW! WILL YOU LOOK AT THAT! THEY SEEM TO BE DANCING!
NO SHOOT! WE SURRENDER!
THIS TIME THEY WERE TOO BUSY TO AMBUSH OUR CHOPPER!
YEAH, BIFFO. THEY HAD A FEW PROBLEMS OF THEIR OWN! LET'S GO TELL GIZMO HIS PLAN WORKED!
Back at base—
YEAH, I THOUGHT IT WOULD WORK, SIR. WHEN YOU DOUSED THOSE GOOKS WITH MY EXTRA STRONG MIXTURE OF ITCHING POWDER ALL THEY COULD DO WAS SCRATCH!
NO WONDER THE BRASS THOUGHT THE LIEUTENANT HERE WAS SOME KIND OF NUT!
IN THIS SQUADRON WE'RE ALL NUTS OF ONE SORT OR ANOTHER — SO ONE MORE WON'T MAKE ANY DIFFERENCE!
The End

By the First World War, balloons had become vast airships and both sides used them for bombing raids. The Germans persisted for the duration of the war and London and the south of England were subjected to raids by the mighty airships.
R